FIELD THEORY

ALLEN NUSSBAUM
University of Minnesota

CHARLES E. MERRILL BOOKS, INC., COLUMBUS, OHIO

For Liz, Pete,
Pudge, and Davey

Library of Congress Catalog Card Number: 66-14408

PRINTED IN THE UNITED STATES OF AMERICA

SERIES EDITOR

GLEN A. RICHARDSON
Worcester, Massachusetts

The Merrill Electronics Series is a new approach to the ever-growing problem of providing an appropriate textbook for basic electronics courses at the undergraduate level. A rapidly changing electronics technology leads to many proposed approaches and arrangements of topics in electronics courses. A serious problem arises in the effort to implement well-conceived course plans with suitable textbooks. Too often there is no single book that treats the material in the desired manner and includes the desired topics at an acceptable level.

The Merrill Electronics Series is planned as an integrated group of high quality texts, each complete within itself except for required background material, each covering a single or narrow range of topics, and each preparing a student for the topics that would follow naturally. A graded series of problems is provided for each book. A consistent set of standard letter and graphic symbols is used throughout the series.

The Series is open-ended. New books may be added as developments in electronics indicate a need. Similarly, books in the Series may be revised or replaced in response to a need. The concept of several small books, each covering a narrow range of topics, gives a flexibility that cannot be achieved in the production of full-length textbooks.

GLEN A. RICHARDSON
Worcester, Massachusetts

Author's Preface

This introduction to the theory of electromagnetic fields starts with the basic experimental laws and shows how they lead to Maxwell's equations in a logical and consistent way. Applications related to the behavior of circuit elements and electron devices are incorporated in this development.

By way of background, it is assumed that the student has the following preparation:

(1) An introductory engineering physics course
(2) Calculus and elementary differential equations
(3) Some training in vector algebra and the use of the vector differential operators.

For those readers unfamiliar with vector methods, it is suggested that they refer to *A Short Course in Vector Analysis* by Kenneth S. Miller, Charles E. Merrill Books, Inc., Columbus, Ohio (1962). An extensive discussion of the physical significance of the vector differential operators will be found in the present author's *Electromagnetic Fields for Engineers and Scientists*, Prentice-Hall, Inc., Englewood Cliffs, N. J. (1965). In preparing the treatment given here, I have drawn heavily on the sources acknowledged in the earlier volume, and would like to restate my appreciation for the assistance given.

ALLEN NUSSBAUM

January, 1966 *Minneapolis, Minnesota*

Table of Contents

1 Electrostatic Fields in Free Space

1.1 Fundamental and Derived Quantities

All of the quantities used in science and engineering may be expressed in terms of a small number of fundamental ones. Modern electromagnetic technology is based on the use of *length* (l), *mass* (m), *time* (t), and *charge* (q) as the fundamental quantities, and the units of measurement are the *meter* (m), the *kilogram* (kg), the *second* (sec), and the *coulomb* (coul), respectively. This choice is called the *MKSC system;* other systems are possible, however, and the one generally used in research is the *symmetrical CGS system.* The fundamental quantities are taken as length (in cm), mass (in gm), and time (in sec). The unit of charge is defined in terms of the force between two charges at a given distance, and Table I shows that it has dimensions of $m^{1/2}l^{3/2}/t$. Some typical quantities in the two systems are shown in Table I. The MKSC system is seen to be compatible with units, such as the volt and watt, which have been in common use in engineering for many years.

TABLE I

Quantity	Symbol	CGS Unit	MKSC Unit
Length	l	cm	m
Mass	m	gm	kg
Time	t	sec	sec
Force	F	gm-cm/sec^2 = dyne	kg-m/sec^2 = newton
Work	W	dyne-cm = erg	newton-m = joule
Charge	q	(erg-cm)$^{1/2}$	coul
Electric field	$\mathbf{E}$	(erg/cm^3)$^{1/2}$	newton/coul = volt/m
Electric potential	V	(erg/cm)$^{1/2}$	joule/coul = volt
Electric current	I	(erg-cm)$^{1/2}$/sec	coul/sec = amphere
Magnetic field	$\mathbf{B}$	(erg/cm^3)$^{1/2}$ = gauss	kg/coul-sec = webers/m^2
Resistance	R	sec/cm	volt/ampere = ohm
Capacitance	C	cm	coul/volt = farad
Inductance	L	sec^2/cm	volt-sec/ampere = henry
Permittivity	ϵ_r	(dimensionless)	farad/m
Permeability	μ_r	(dimensionless)	henry/m
Power	P	erg/sec	joule/sec = watt

1.2 Coulomb's Law

Let us consider two charged particles in a vacuum and separated by a fixed distance r. The *quantity* or *magnitude* q of charge is that property of either particle to which the mutual force between them is directly proportional, or

$$F \propto q_1 q_2 \tag{1–1}$$

where q_1 and q_2 are the respective charges on each particle. Coulomb showed experimentally that for two given charges with a separation r, which we now permit to vary, the force obeys the inverse-square law

$$F \propto 1/r^2 \tag{1–2}$$

Combining (1–1) and (1–2) and introducing a proportionality constant C,

$$F = Cq_1q_2/r^2 \tag{1–3}$$

and this relation is known as *Coulomb's law*.

A convenient natural standard of electric charge is furnished by the electron. The unit of charge is designated as a *coulomb*, and the magnitude of the charge e on the electron is arbitrarily set at 1.60×10^{-19} coulomb to agree with other electrical units already in use. In addition, the electron's charge is assigned a negative sign, so that

$$-e = -1.60 \times 10^{-19} \text{ coulomb} \tag{1–4}$$

It is found convenient to replace C with a new constant ϵ_v related to C by

$$C = \frac{1}{4\pi\epsilon_v} \tag{1-5}$$

so that (1–3) assumes the form

$$F = \frac{q_1 q_2}{4\pi\epsilon_v r^2} \tag{1-6}$$

The quantity ϵ_v is called the *permittivity of free space*, and its value can be determined experimentally (although indirectly). It is found that the force between two point-charges of magnitude 1 coulomb at a distance of 1 meter is about 9×10^9 newtons (roughly equal to 10^6 tons). Then from (1–6)

$$\epsilon_v = \frac{1}{36\pi \times 10^9} = 8.85 \times 10^{-12} \frac{\text{coulomb}^2}{\text{newton-meter}^2} \tag{1-7}$$

If we define an electrical unit called the *farad* by

$$1 \text{ farad} = 1 \frac{\text{coulomb}^2}{\text{newton meter}} \tag{1-8}$$

then

$$\epsilon_v = 8.85 \times 10^{-12} \text{ farad/m} \tag{1-9}$$

Finally, it should be mentioned that the factor 4π in (1–5) is used to simplify Maxwell's equations, and its inclusion in Coulomb's law leads to what are known as *rationalized* MKSC units.

1.3 Electric Fields

We know that an electric charge exerts either an attractive or a repulsive force on all other charges in its vicinity, provided that there is no intervening shielding. The entire region of influence of a charge is called its *electric field* and its magnitude is specified by a quantity called the *electric field intensity* **E**. Also, we picture a field in terms of *lines of force*—the paths along which a positive charge is urged. Consider the field due to a charge q_1 exerting a force **F** on another charge q_2. The field intensity **E** is then defined as the force per unit charge exerted on a given charge in the field, or

$$\mathbf{E} = \frac{\mathbf{F}}{q} \text{ newtons/coulomb} \tag{1-10}$$

(where we are assuming that no mass is associated with the charges). If we write Coulomb's law (1–6) in vector form as

$$\mathbf{F} = \frac{q_1 q_2 \mathbf{r}_0}{4\pi\epsilon_v r^2} \tag{1-11}$$

where $\mathbf{r}_0$ is a unit vector along $\mathbf{r}$, then (1–10) becomes (Fig. 1-1)

$$\mathbf{E} = \frac{q_1 \mathbf{r}_0}{4\pi\epsilon_v r^2}. \tag{1–12}$$

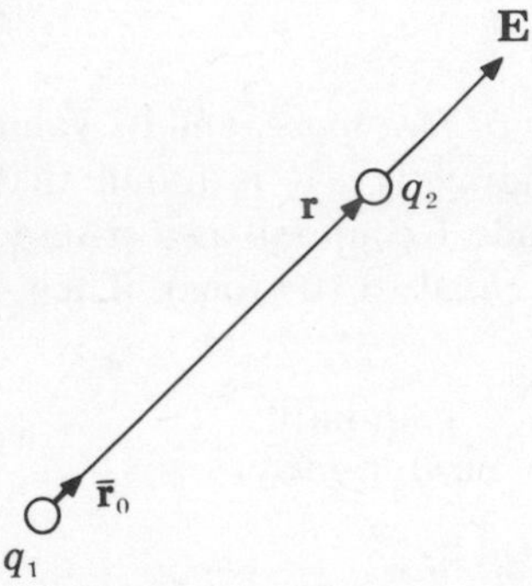

Fig. 1-1 The electric field at a location **r** due to a point-charge q_1.

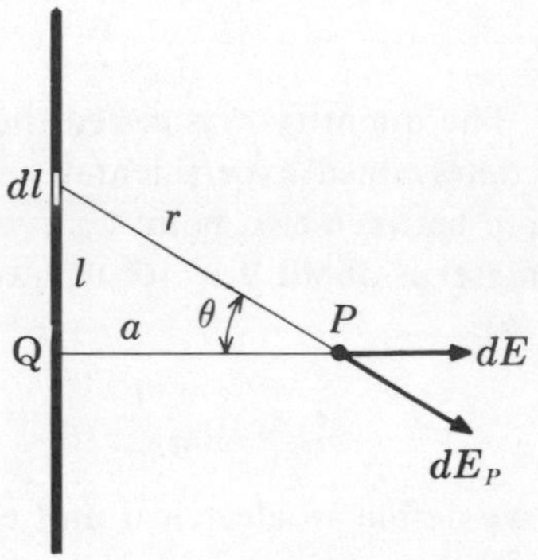

Fig. 1-2 Calculation of the field due to a line charge.

Example 1-1 Field Due to a Line-Charge

Figure 1-2 shows an infinite charged wire with a uniform charge λ per unit length. To find the field at any point P, select an element of length dl at a distance l from the perpendicular QP. The charge on the element dl is λdl and by Eq. (1–12), the field at P is

$$dE_P = \frac{\lambda dl}{4\pi\epsilon_v r^2}$$

For each element dl, there is a corresponding one at a distance l on the other side of Q, so that the resultant field dE is normal to the wire. Hence

$$dE = dE_P \cos\theta.$$

Using

$$l = a \tan\theta, \qquad dl = a \sec^2\theta \, d\theta, \qquad a = r\cos\theta$$

gives

$$E = \frac{\lambda}{4\pi\epsilon_v} \int_{-\pi/2}^{\pi/2} \frac{a \sec^2\theta \, d\theta}{(a/\cos\theta)^2} \cos\theta = \frac{\lambda}{2\pi\epsilon_v a} \tag{1–13}$$

Hence, in this example, the field is inversely proportional to the first power of the distance, whereas for a point-charge, by (1–12), it varies as l/r^2.

Problem 1-1

Find the field E at any point equidistant from the ends of a short wire of length $2L$ having a uniform charge λ coulombs/meter. Show that your result agrees with (1-13) when L is allowed to become very large.

Problem 1-2

Consider two charged wires, each having the same charge λ per unit length. Show that the force per unit length between them is

$$F_1 = \frac{\lambda^2}{2\pi\epsilon_v a} \tag{1-14}$$

where a is their separation.

Problem 1-3

An infinite plane has a uniform surface charge density of σ coulombs/meter^2. Using polar coordinates and the reasoning employed in Example 1-1, show that the field in front of the plane is given by

$$E = \frac{\sigma}{2\epsilon_v} \tag{1-15}$$

Problem 1-4

A point P is 1 meter in front of a point O on an infinite uniformly charged plane. How much of the area surrounding O is responsible for half the field intensity measured at P?

Problem 1-5

A uniformly charged wire, with a total charge q, is bent into the shape of a semicircle of radius R. Show that the field at the center is given by

$$E = \frac{q}{2\pi^2 \epsilon_v R^2}$$

1.4 Electrostatic Flux and Gauss' Law

The word *flux* in ancient times meant the flow or movement of a fluid. Its mathematical meaning is somewhat different, although related to the idea of fluid motion. Before stating this definition, we should be point out that a surface can be represented by a vector. For an elementary area dA, we first insure that it is small enough so that it is approximately flat. We then construct a vector $d\mathbf{A}$ which is normal to the elementary area and whose length is numerically equal to the magnitude of the area. The sense of $d\mathbf{A}$ is chosen so that it points outward for a closed surface.

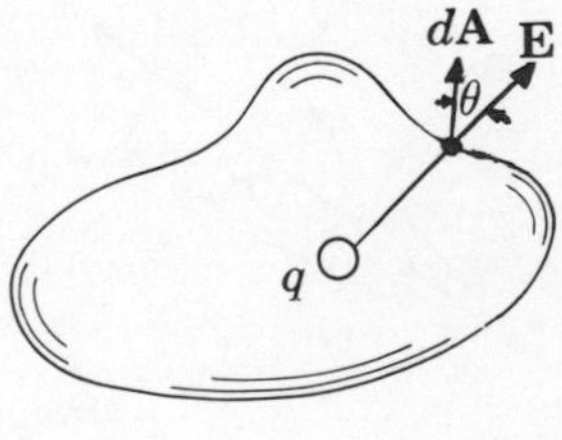

Fig. 1-3 Calculation of the flux over an arbitrary closed surface.

We now define the *flux* ψ of a vector $\mathbf{D}$ over a surface A by the relation

$$\psi = \int \mathbf{D} \cdot d\mathbf{A} \tag{1-16}$$

To obtain a feel for the physical meaning of this definition, let us consider the flux of the electric field over some surface A in the field. Figure 1-3 shows an arbitrary closed surface (think of a potato) surrounding a charge q. The flux of $\mathbf{E}$ over this surface is

$$\psi = \oint \mathbf{E} \cdot d\mathbf{A} \tag{1-17}$$

where the special symbol $\oint$ denotes that we are integrating over a closed surface. In words, Eq. (1–17) states that we first find the quantity $E\,dA\cos\theta$ at each point on A and then we "add" all these quantities by integrating over the entire surface. Since $d\mathbf{A}$ is everywhere normal to A, the factor $E\cos\theta$ is the normal component E_n of $\mathbf{E}$, and (1–17) can also be written

$$\psi = \oint E_n dA \tag{1-18}$$

Intuitively, the flux ψ can be regarded as the total "flow" of these normal components of the lines of force from q outward across A, although what we have here is a purely static system.

We have previously shown, in Eq. (1–12), that the field $\mathbf{E}$ due to the charge q is given by

$$\mathbf{E} = \frac{q\mathbf{r}_0}{4\pi\epsilon_v r^2} \tag{1-19}$$

Combining this with (1–18) gives

$$\psi = \frac{q}{4\pi\epsilon_v}\oint\frac{\cos\theta\, dA}{r^2} \tag{1-20}$$

This integral can be evaluated by introducing the concept of *solid angle* ω which we define in connection with Fig. 1-4. The solid angle at the vertex of a cone is the surface area which the cone intercepts on a sphere of unit radius. Consider now a cone with an infinitesimal base of area A tilted at an angle θ. The projection of dA on a sphere of radius r is $dA\cos\theta$. Hence, the solid angle $d\omega$ subtended by the cone is given by

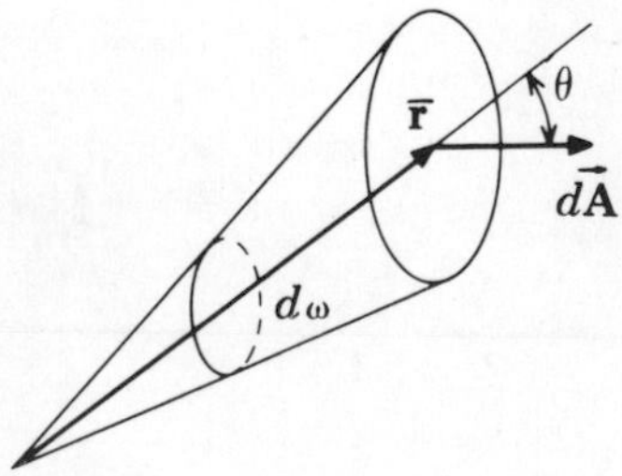

Fig. 1-4 An element of solid angle.

$$\frac{dA\cos\theta}{r^2} = \frac{d\omega}{1^2} \tag{1-21}$$

since the area intercepted by the cone on a sphere of radius r is proportional to r^2. Now *spherical radian* is defined as the solid angle subtended by an area equal to r^2 (in analogy with the circular radian, which is an angle subtended by an arc of length r). This means that there are $4\pi r^2/r^2$, or 4π, spherical radians to a sphere. Using this fact and Eq. (1–21), Eq. (1–20) becomes

$$\psi = \frac{q}{4\pi\epsilon_v}\int_0^{4\pi} d\omega = \frac{q}{\epsilon_v}$$

or

$$\oint \mathbf{E}\cdot d\mathbf{A} = \frac{q}{\epsilon_v} \tag{1–22}$$

This relation is known as *Gauss' law*.

If we write Gauss' law in the form

$$\oint (\epsilon_v \mathbf{E})\cdot d\mathbf{A} = q \tag{1–23}$$

then the left-hand side, by (1–16), is the flux of the quantity $\epsilon_v\mathbf{E}$, known as the *electric displacement* **D**, or

$$\mathbf{D} = \epsilon_v \mathbf{E} \tag{1–24}$$

Gauss' law then states that flux of the electric displacement over a closed surface equals the amount of enclosed charge. The flux of **D** is often referred to as the *electrostatic flux*, and we shall reserve the symbol ψ for this quantity. There are, of course, an infinite number of lines of force radiating from every point-charge, but in visualizing electrostatic relations it is helpful to arbitrarily set this number equal to the flux of **D**. Then, by Gauss' law, (1–23), the number of lines of force equals the size of the charge in coulombs, and Gauss' law may also be thought of as a statement of the conservation of lines of force. That is, all the lines which leave a single point-charge must cross any closed surface placed around that charge. Another important point to consider is that we were able to replace the integrand in (1–20) by $d\omega$ only because of the inverse-square character of Coulomb's law. Hence, Gauss' law is a consequence of Coulomb's law and, in fact, replaces it as one of the fundamental experimental laws of electromagnetism. However, it should be strongly emphasized at this point that we have shown how Coulomb's law leads to Gauss' law only for charges which are fixed in both magnitude and position. Both of these laws are valid even when these quantities are variable; the experimental proof follows indirectly from Maxwell's equations, which we shall discuss later.

We can extend (1–22) in several ways. If the closed surface surrounds several point-charges of various values or sign, then we may write

$$\oint \mathbf{E}\cdot d\mathbf{A} = \frac{\Sigma q_i}{\epsilon_v}$$

since each charge contributes independently to the integral. If the enclosed charge is finite in size, with a charge ρ per unit volume, then (1–22) becomes

$$\oint \mathbf{E}\cdot d\mathbf{A} = \int \left(\frac{\rho}{\epsilon_v}\right) dV \tag{1–25}$$

Now, consider a point-charge q placed *outside* the closed surface. From

Fig. 1–5, we see that each line of force cuts the surface twice. At the intersection closer to q the vector **E** points inward, and at the farther one it points outward. The integral $\oint \mathbf{E}\cdot d\mathbf{A}$ can be divided into two parts, corresponding to regions where **E** points inward or outward. The two regions will subtend the same solid angle but their signs will be opposite, so that the total integral vanishes. Hence, Gauss' law states that the flux of $\epsilon_v \mathbf{E}$ over a closed surface equals the magnitude of the charge *inside* the surface.

Problem 1-6

Give the geometrical reason for the statement that the integral vanishes.

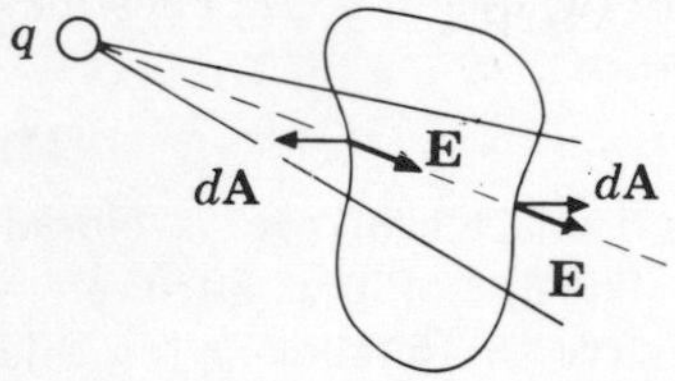

Fig. 1-5 Gauss' law for an exterior charge.

As a final point, let us briefly consider the nature of **D**. To do this, we apply dimensional analysis. Using square brackets to denote "has dimensions of," we see that velocity v, for example, in terms of length l and time t, can be expressed as

$$[v] = \left[\frac{l}{t}\right] \tag{1–26}$$

which is read "the dimensions of velocity are length per unit time." Similarly, for force

$$[F] = \left[\frac{ml}{t^2}\right] \tag{1–27}$$

and the electric field intensity is

$$[E] = \left[\frac{F}{q}\right] = \left[\frac{ml}{t^2 q}\right] \tag{1–28}$$

Then, by (1–12),

$$[\epsilon_v] = \left[\frac{q}{El^2}\right] = \left[\frac{q^2 t^2}{ml^3}\right] \tag{1–29}$$

(Note that the constant 4π is dimensionless and need not be considered.) From (1–24) and (1–29), we have

$$[D] = [q/l^2]$$

so that **D** has units of coulombs/meter^2. This explains why it is sometimes called the *flux density*, since it represents the number of lines of force per unit area. We shall consider the quantity **D** in more detail in Chapter 2, and it will be shown there that definition (1–24) is the special form, applicable to a vacuum, of a more general relation. A table of dimensions for key quantities is given in Appendix B.

Example 1-2 Gauss' Law Applied to a Sphere

We shall use Gauss' law to find the field **E** that is due to a uniformly charged sphere. The closed surface to which we shall apply the law is chosen as a sphere of arbitrary radius R concentric to, and surrounding, the charged sphere (Fig. 1-6). By symmetry, **E** is uniform and radial over the charged sphere and over the Gaussian surface. By (1–22),

$$\frac{q}{\epsilon_v} = \oint \mathbf{E} \cdot d\mathbf{A} = \mathbf{E} \oint dA = E(4\pi R^2)$$

or

$$E = \frac{q}{4\pi\epsilon_v R^2} \tag{1-30}$$

This expression agrees with the corresponding relation (1–12) for a point-charge and shows that the fields are identical in the two cases for the region beyond the surface of the sphere.

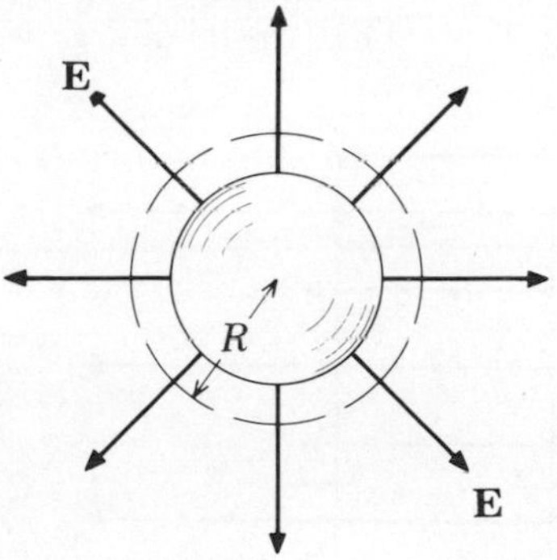

Fig. 1-6 Gauss' law applied to a uniformly charged sphere.

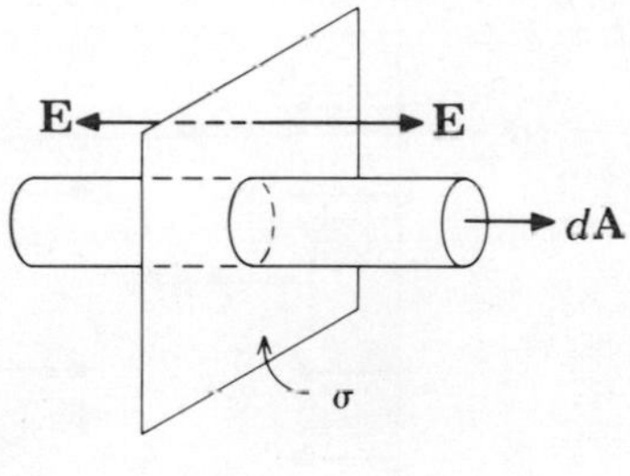

Fig. 1-7 Gaussian surface for a thin charged sheet.

Example 1-3 Gauss' Law Applied to a Charged Plane

The application of Gauss' law to a charged plane involves a concept which we have not previously considered, and this is that an infinitesimally-thin planar charge cannot really exist. We shall, however, use this idea for mathematical convenience and then discuss the modifications necessary in practice. In Fig. 1-7, we show a thin charged sheet with a uniform charge of σ coulombs/meter^2. The surface to which we wish to apply Gauss' law is chosen as a right cylinder of cross section dA. The flux integral has non-vanishing contributions only from the ends of the cylinder, and hence,

$$2E\,dA = \frac{\sigma\,dA}{\epsilon_v}$$

or

$$E = \frac{\sigma}{2\epsilon_v}$$

agreeing with (1–15).

Suppose that we now do the same calculation for a metal sheet of finite thickness. A conducting sheet can be charged only on the surface, and there is no internal field. If we construct the cylinder so that one end lies outside the sheet (Fig. 1–8a) and one end lies inside, then

$$E\,dA = \frac{\sigma\,dA}{\epsilon_v}$$

or

$$E = \frac{\sigma}{\epsilon_v} \tag{1–31}$$

which appears to contradict the previous result, Eq. (1–15). To resolve this difficulty, we must realize that a charged metal sheet, with a small but finite thickness, will appear as shown in Fig. 1–8b. That is, the charge will

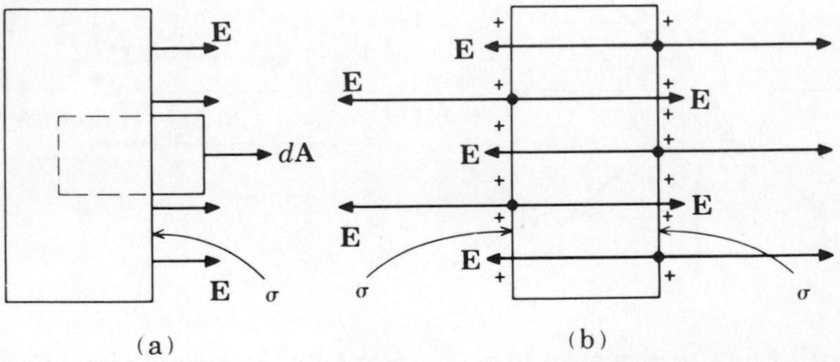

Fig. 1-8 Field for a metal plate of finite thickness.

be distributed across both faces and there will be a field across each face due both to its own charge and to the charge on the other face. Inside the metal sheet, these fields cancel in pairs, producing a field-free region. In front of either face, the total field E is the sum of the field $\sigma/2\epsilon_v$ from each of the two faces, so that for a thick metal sheet,

$$E = \frac{\sigma}{\epsilon_v}$$

which verifies the correctness of (1–31).

1.5 Electrostatic Potential

We now wish to introduce the concept of energy into our treatment of electrostatics. *Energy* W is defined as the ability of a body to do work and, as for work, the unit of energy is the *joule.* The energy which a body possesses by virtue of its position is called *potential energy* V; that which is due to its motion is *kinetic energy* T. We can find a general formula for kinetic energy by considering a force F acting along the x-axis and imparting a speed v to a body originally at rest. Then the work done is

$$W = \int F dx = \int \frac{dp}{dt} dx = T$$

For a constant mass

$$T = m \int \frac{dv}{dt} dx = m \int_0^v v dv = \frac{1}{2} mv^2 \tag{1-32}$$

Consider now the motion of a charge q in an electric field $\mathbf{E}$. We define a quantity called the *electrostatic potential difference* V as the work per unit charge required to move q from one place to another in the field. If this quantity of work is W, then

$$V = \frac{W}{q} \tag{1-33}$$

This shows that the unit of V is the joule/coulomb, and this unit is called a *volt*. (It is customary to refer to V as the *voltage*.) From (1-10) and (1-33), we have

$$V = \int \left(\frac{\mathbf{F}}{q}\right) \cdot d\mathbf{l} = \int \mathbf{E} \cdot d\mathbf{l}$$

However, we would like to define the potential difference in such a way that V *increases* when work is done *on* the displaced charge. For example, suppose that we have two positive charges q_1 and q_2. If q_1 is fixed, then we must do work to move q_2 closer to q_1, and this process should represent an increase in V. But this situation means that the direction of motion is opposed to the field, and hence we write

$$V = -\int \mathbf{E} \cdot d\mathbf{l} \tag{1-34}$$

where the negative sign indicates that V increases when $d\mathbf{l}$ and $\mathbf{E}$ have opposite signs.

Because the charge $-e$ on the electron is such a small fraction of a coulomb ($e = 1.6 \times 10^{-19}$ coul), the joule is an inconvenient unit of work or energy for problems involving the motion of electrons in solids. Hence, we introduce a smaller energy unit called the *electron-volt* (e-v), which is defined as the amount of energy necessary to move an electron through a difference in potential of 1 volt. The work done in such a process can then be expressed as

$$W = eV = (1.6 \times 10^{-19}\,\text{coul})(1\,\text{volt})$$
$$= 1.6 \times 10^{-19}\,\text{joule} = 1\,\text{e-v} \tag{1-35}$$

and this gives the conversion factor between joules and electron-volts.

If we now introduce the vector differential operator known as the *gradient* by the definition

$$\textbf{grad}\, V = \nabla V = \mathbf{i}\frac{\partial}{\partial x} + \mathbf{j}\frac{\partial}{\partial y} + \mathbf{k}\frac{\partial}{\partial z}$$

then we can show that (1–34) may be solved for $\mathbf{E}$ to obtain

$$\mathbf{E} = -\,\textbf{grad}\, V \tag{1-36}$$

To prove this relation, we substitute into (1–34), obtaining

$$V = \int \textbf{grad}\, V \cdot d\mathbf{l}$$

But this is an identity, since the definition of the differential dV of V is

$$dV = \frac{\partial V}{\partial x}dx + \frac{\partial V}{\partial y}dy + \frac{\partial V}{\partial z}dz$$

where

$$d\mathbf{l} = \mathbf{i}\,dx + \mathbf{j}\,dy + \mathbf{k}\,dz$$

Example 1-4 Potential Associated with Point-Charge or Sphere

We have shown that the field due to a point-charge or a uniformly charged sphere is given by

$$E = q/4\pi\epsilon_v r^2 \tag{1-12), (1-30}$$

where r is the distance from the point or the center of the sphere. Let us now find the electrostatic potential difference V between two concentric spherical surfaces of radius R_1 and R_2, respectively (Fig. 1-9). Surfaces over which the potential has a constant value are known as *equipotentials*. Let the sphere have a positive charge q and let us move a positive point-charge from R_2 to R_1, so that V increases in the process. Then by Eq. (1–34)

$$V = -\int_{R_2}^{R_1} \mathbf{E}\cdot d\mathbf{l} = -\int_{R_2}^{R_1} E dr = \frac{-q}{4\pi\epsilon_v}\int_{R_2}^{R_1}\frac{dr}{r^2} = \frac{q}{4\pi\epsilon_v}\frac{1}{r}\Big|_{R_2}^{R_1}$$
$$= \frac{q}{4\pi\epsilon_v}\left(\frac{1}{R_1} - \frac{1}{R_2}\right) \tag{1-37}$$

If we had brought the small charge in from an infinite distance ($R_2 = \infty$), then (1–37) would become

$$V = q/4\pi\epsilon_v R_1 \tag{1-38}$$

and we can refer to V as the *absolute electrostatic potential.* Note that in using this concept, we must specify that V designates the potential due to a sphere or a point and that the zero or reference level is at infinity. For other geometries, the reference level is not the same and we must be careful that the location has been explicitly given.

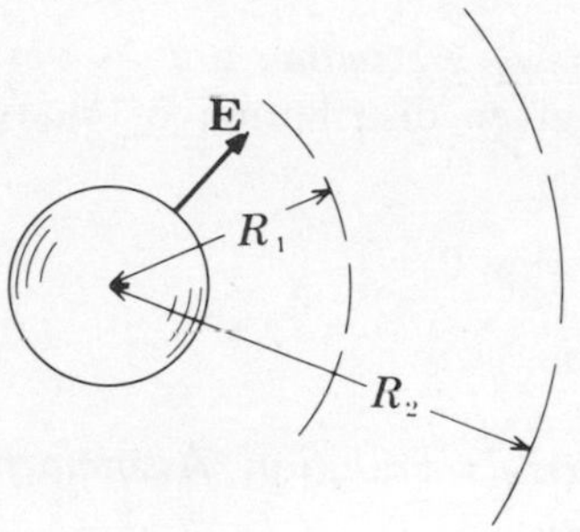

Fig. 1-9 Equipotentials for a charged sphere.

1.6 Laplace's and Poisson's Equations

Equation (A–11) of the appendix is known as the *divergence* or *Gauss' theorem;* it shows the connection between the divergence of a vector **D** when integrated throughout a volume V and the flux of **D** integrated over the bounding surface A of this volume. This theorem is

$$\int \operatorname{div} \mathbf{D}\, dV = \oint \mathbf{D} \cdot d\mathbf{A} \tag{A–11}$$

Combining this with Gauss' law in the form (1–25) gives

$$\int \operatorname{div} \mathbf{E}\, dV = \int \left(\frac{\rho}{\epsilon_v}\right) dV$$

If this relation holds for an arbitrarily small volume dV, then we may equate the integrands to obtain

$$\operatorname{div} \mathbf{E} = \rho/\epsilon_v \tag{1–39}$$

This equation is one of a set of four known as *Maxwell's equations;* we have established its validity here only for static fields. The situation for time-varying fields will be considered in Chapter 3.

If we now combine the two Eqs. (1–36) and (1–39), we obtain

$$\operatorname{div} \mathbf{grad}\, V = -\frac{\rho}{\epsilon_v}$$

or

$$\nabla^2 V = -\frac{\rho}{\epsilon_v} \tag{1–40}$$

where the vector differential operator div **grad** or ∇^2 is called the *Laplacian.* In rectangular coordinates only it is defined as

$$\text{div}\,\mathbf{grad} = \nabla^2 = \frac{\partial^2}{\partial x^2} + \frac{\partial^2}{\partial y^2} + \frac{\partial^2}{\partial z^2} \tag{1-41}$$

Expressions for the Laplacian in spherical and cylindrical coordinates are given in the appendix.

Equation (1–40) is known as *Poisson's equation* and is very useful in determining the potential due to a given distribution of charge. For the special case $\rho = 0$, (1–40) reduces to

$$\nabla^2 V = 0 \tag{1-42}$$

which is known as *Laplace's equation.*

Example 1-5 Solution of Laplace's Equation Assuming Spherical Symmetry

Consider a sphere of radius R with a uniform charge q. By symmetry, the electrostatic potential V outside the sphere depends only on the distance r from the center. That is

$$\frac{\partial V}{\partial \theta} = \frac{\partial^2 V}{\partial \theta^2} = \frac{\partial V}{\partial \phi} = \frac{\partial^2 V}{\partial \phi^2} = 0$$

Hence, Laplace's equation (1–42) in spherical coordinates reduces to the ordinary differential equation

$$\frac{1}{r^2}\frac{d}{dr}\left(r^2\frac{dV}{dr}\right) = 0$$

where we have used (A–21). Differentiating the quantity in parentheses gives

$$\frac{d^2 V}{dr^2} + \frac{2}{r}\frac{dV}{dr} = 0 \tag{1-43}$$

Now introduce the notation

$$\frac{dV}{dr} = V' \tag{1-44}$$

so that (1–43) becomes

$$\frac{dV'}{V'} = -\frac{2dr}{r}$$

Integrating, we obtain

$$\ln V' = -2\ln r + C$$

where C is a constant of integration, which we write as

$$C = \ln A$$

and A is another arbitrary constant. Then

$$\ln V' = \ln\left(\frac{A}{r^2}\right)$$

or

$$dV' = \frac{Adr}{r^2}$$

and

$$V = -\frac{A}{R} + B \tag{1–45}$$

where B is a second integration constant. To identify A and B, we must specify the *boundary conditions*, which are the restrictions imposed on the solution (1–45) for special values of r. The first boundary condition is the requirement that $V = 0$ at $r = \infty$ to agree with the convention adopted in Example 1-4. Substituting these values into (1–45), we obtain

$$B = 0$$

If the constant value of V on the surface of the sphere is denoted by V_R, then again by (1–45)

$$V_R = -\frac{A}{R}$$

or

$$A = -RV_R$$

and

$$V = \frac{V_R R}{r} \tag{1–46}$$

This is as far as we can go with Laplace's equation. We note, however, that our solution agrees in form with (1–38) and if we use this equation to determine V_R, obtaining

$$V_R = \frac{q}{4\pi\epsilon_v R}$$

then (1–46) becomes

$$V = \frac{q}{4\pi\epsilon_v r} \tag{1–47}$$

which is the inverse first-power dependence we have previously found, using more elementary methods.

Example 1-6 Conducting Sphere in a Uniform Electric Field

A metal sphere of radius a with no charge on it is placed in a uniform electric field $\mathbf{E}_0$ (Fig. 1-10). As we would expect, the sphere distorts the

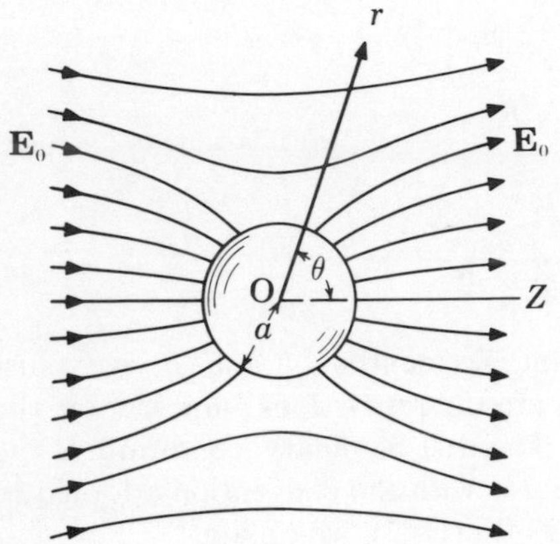

Fig. 1-10 A conducting sphere in an originally uniform field. (From A. F. Kip, *Fundamentals of Electricity and Magnetism*, McGraw-Hill Book Co., Inc., 1962, with permission.)

field, the result being shown in the figure. To determine the nature of the lines of force and equipotentials, we can use Laplace's equation in spherical coordinates. It is convenient mathematically to choose the z-axis parallel to $\mathbf{E}_0$. and through the center of the sphere. Since the field and potential will be symmetrical with respect to this axis, this means that derivatives with respect to φ vanish and by (A–21), Laplace's equation becomes

$$\frac{\partial}{\partial r}\left(r^2 \frac{\partial V}{\partial r}\right) + \frac{1}{\sin\theta}\frac{\partial}{\partial\theta}\left(\sin\theta\,\frac{\partial V}{\partial\theta}\right) = 0 \qquad \textbf{(1–48)}$$

We may solve this equation by the method of *separation of variables.* The potential V depends on r and θ, and we shall assume that it can be written as the product of two new functions $R(r)$ and $\Theta(\theta)$, where R depends only on r and Θ depends only on θ. That is

$$V(r, \theta) = R(r)\Theta(\theta) \qquad \textbf{(1–49)}$$

We then see that

$$\frac{\partial}{\partial r}\left(r^2 \frac{\partial V}{\partial r}\right) = \Theta\,\frac{d}{dr}\left(r^2 \frac{dR}{dr}\right)$$

and

$$\frac{1}{\sin\theta}\frac{\partial}{\partial\theta}\left(\sin\theta\,\frac{\partial V}{\partial\theta}\right) = \frac{R}{\sin\theta}\frac{d}{d\theta}\left(\sin\theta\,\frac{d\Theta}{d\theta}\right)$$

Upon dividing through by the product $R\Theta$, we obtain

$$\frac{1}{R}\frac{d}{dr}\left(r^2\frac{dR}{dr}\right) = -\frac{1}{\Theta\sin\theta}\frac{d}{d\theta}\left(\sin\theta\frac{d\Theta}{d\theta}\right)$$

The left-hand side of this equation depends only upon r, and the right-hand side only upon θ. The only way for the two sides to be equal for arbitrary values of r and θ is for them both to be equal to a constant C, since both r and θ are completely independent variables. Hence, we obtain the following two ordinary differential equations

$$\frac{d}{dr}\left(r^2\frac{dR}{dr}\right) - CR = 0 \tag{1–50}$$

and

$$\frac{d}{d\theta}\left(\sin\theta\frac{d\Theta}{d\theta}\right) + C(\sin\theta)\Theta = 0 \tag{1–51}$$

from the separated partial differential equation (1–48). The r-equation (1–50) can be solved by trying a solution

$$R = r^n$$

Then

$$\frac{dR}{dr} = nr^{n-1}$$

and

$$\frac{d}{dr}(nr^2r^{n-1}) = (n+1)nr^n$$

so that

$$(n+1)n - C = 0$$

Using the quadratic formula, we obtain

$$n = \frac{-1 \pm \sqrt{1+4C}}{2} \tag{1–52}$$

This result can be simplified if we let C have the form

$$C = l(l+1) \tag{1–53}$$

where l is some new arbitrary constant. Then (1–52) becomes

$$n = \frac{-1 \pm \sqrt{4l^2+4l+1}}{2} = \left.\begin{matrix} l \\ -(l+1) \end{matrix}\right\} \tag{1–54}$$

Since the solution of a second-order differential equation has two integration constants, we see that the complete solution of (1–50) is

$$R = Ar^l + \frac{B}{r^{l+1}} \tag{1–55}$$

The θ-equation (1–51) is known as the *Legendre equation* and is much more difficult to solve. We can show that it has an infinite number of solutions, but rather than solve it analytically, we shall guess at the appropriate answer. We realize from Fig. 1–10 that at a long distance from the sphere, the field **E** has its undistorted value $\mathbf{E}_0$, and the corresponding potential is

$$V_z = -E_0 z = -E_0 r \cos\theta \tag{1–56}$$

Now any solution we find should have this form for large r, and this leads us to try $\Theta = \cos\theta$ as a solution to (1–51), obtaining

$$-2\sin\theta\cos\theta + l(l+1)\cos\theta\sin\theta = 0$$

or

$$l = 1, -2$$

The product of the two solutions is then

$$V = R\Theta = Ar\cos\theta + \frac{B\cos\theta}{r^2} \tag{1–57}$$

and direct substitution of this result into (1–48) verifies that it is the solution we were seeking. To determine A and B, we need two boundary conditions. One of them has already been mentioned, namely Eq. (1–56), so that

$$V = -E_0 r\cos\theta \quad \text{for} \quad r = \infty \tag{1–58}$$

The other we will chose as the requirement that the surface of the sphere be the reference level, or

$$V = 0 \quad \text{for} \quad r = a \tag{1–59}$$

From these, we find that

$$A = -E_0, \qquad B = E_0 a^3 \tag{1–60}$$

and the solution to Laplace's equation which also satisfies our boundary conditions is

$$V = -\left(1 - \frac{a^3}{r^3}\right)E_0 r\cos\theta \tag{1–61}$$

(It is shown in more advanced texts that there is only one solution to Laplace's equation which satisfies a given set of boundary conditions; that is, the solution is *unique*.) The components of the field **E** are calculated by using (1–36) and (A–18) and are given by

$$\begin{aligned} E_r &= -\frac{\partial V}{\partial r} = \left(1 + \frac{2a^3}{r^3}\right)E_0\cos\theta \\ E_\theta &= -\frac{1}{r}\frac{\partial V}{\partial \theta} = -\left(1 - \frac{a^3}{r^3}\right)E_0\sin\theta \end{aligned} \tag{1–62}$$

Finally, by using Gauss' law, we can find the surface charge σ induced on the sphere by the field. A small cone whose walls lie along the radii is erected at the surface of the sphere (Fig. 1–11). The charge enclosed by this cone has a value $\sigma\, dA$, and the flux $\mathbf{E}\cdot d\mathbf{A}$ is non-zero only over the outer end of the cone. Gauss' law gives

$$\sigma dA/\epsilon_v = E_n\, dA \tag{1–63}$$

or

$$\sigma = \epsilon_v E_n = -\epsilon_v \frac{\partial V}{\partial r}\bigg|_{r=a} = 3\epsilon_v E_0 \cos\theta \tag{1–64}$$

Hence, the induced surface charge is zero along the "equator" of the sphere and a maximum at the poles (the points where the z-axis cuts the sphere).

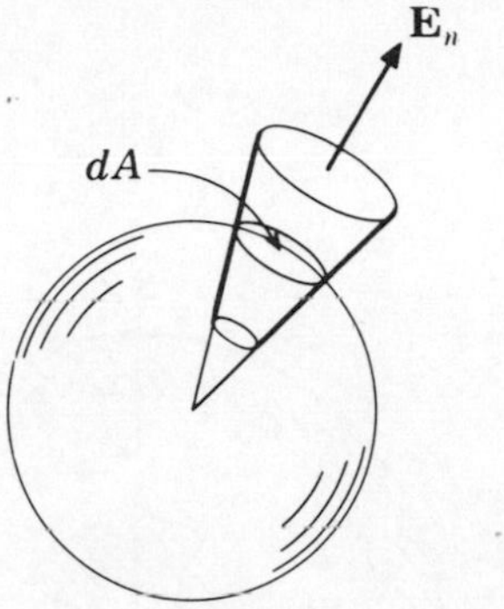

Fig. 1-11 Gaussian surface used to calculate the field normal to the surface of a sphere.

Problem 1-7

(a) Show that a solution to Laplace's equation in cylindrical coordinates is

$$V(r, \theta) = Ar\cos\theta + \frac{B\cos\theta}{r}$$

when V is a function of r and θ only.

(b) Find the solution when V is only a function of r.

Problem 1-8

Two parallel metal plates are a distance D apart. One plate is grounded and the other is charged to a potential V_0. Solve Laplace's equation for the region between the plates. Find $\mathbf{E}$ and show that your expression agrees with the expression obtained from (1–34).

Example 1-7 Concentric Conducting Spheres

Two concentric conducting spheres, with radii as shown in Fig. 1–12, are placed in a uniform field $\mathbf{E}_0$. The inner sphere is given a charge q, and we wish to find the potential and field everywhere

Consider first the region for which $r > a$. The potential will be the sum of individual contributions from the charged inner sphere and from the uncharged outer sphere in a uniform field. Hence, we simply combine the results of Examples 1–5 and 1–6 to obtain

$$V = \frac{q}{4\pi\epsilon_0 r} - E_0\left(1 - \frac{a^3}{r^3}\right) r\cos\theta \tag{1–65}$$

For the region $b < r < a$, the potential is the same as its value at the surface of the outer sphere, since $\mathbf{E} = 0$ for the interior. Hence, by (1–65),

$$V = \frac{q}{4\pi\epsilon_v a} \tag{1–66}$$

For $c < r < b$, there must be a term of the form $q/4\pi\epsilon_v r$ in the expression for V. In order to make this expression reduce to (1–66), it has to have the form

$$V = \frac{q}{4\pi\epsilon_v}\left(\frac{1}{r} + \frac{1}{a} - \frac{1}{b}\right) \qquad \textbf{(1–67)}$$

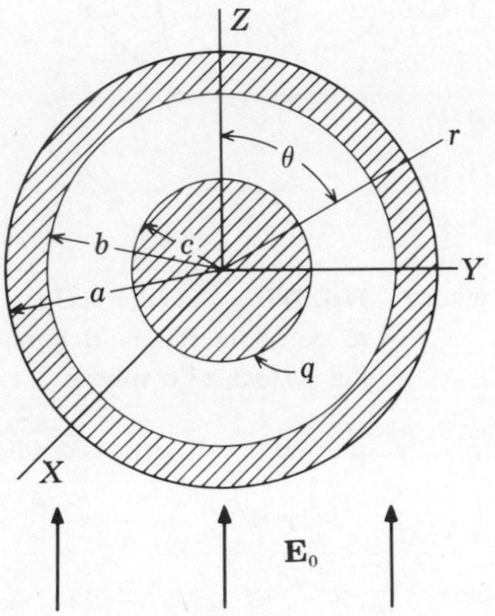

Fig. 1-12 Concentric spheres.

For the interior of the inner sphere, V is again constant, and by (1–67),

$$V = \frac{q}{4\pi\epsilon_v}\left(\frac{1}{c} + \frac{1}{a} - \frac{1}{b}\right) \qquad \textbf{(1–68)}$$

The corresponding fields are obtained from the expressions for the components of the gradient, giving

$$\left.\begin{aligned} E_r &= E_0\left(1 + \frac{2a^3}{r^3}\right)\cos\theta + \frac{q}{4\pi\epsilon_v r^2} \\ E_\theta &= -E_0\left(1 - \frac{a^3}{r^3}\right)\sin\theta \end{aligned}\right\} \quad (r \geqq a) \qquad \textbf{(1–69)}$$

$$E = 0 \qquad (b < r < a) \qquad \textbf{(1–70)}$$

$$\left.\begin{aligned} E_r &= \frac{q}{4\pi\epsilon_v r^2} \\ E_\theta &= 0 \end{aligned}\right\} \quad (c \leqq r \leqq b) \qquad \textbf{(1–71)}$$

$$E = 0 \qquad (r < c) \qquad \textbf{(1–72)}$$

Example 1-8 Solution of Poisson's Equation for a Uniformly Charged Sphere

Consider next a large spherical region of radius R with a uniform charge ρ per unit volume. Then Poisson's equation (1–40) applies to the interior of this sphere, and Laplace's equation (1–42) applies to the exterior, so that

$$\frac{1}{r^2}\frac{d}{dr}\left(r^2\frac{dV}{dr}\right) = \begin{cases} \dfrac{-\rho}{\epsilon_v} & \text{for } r \leqq R \\ 0 & \text{for } r \geqq R \end{cases} \tag{1-73}$$

For the exterior of the sphere ($r > R$), we use the solution (1–45)

$$V_E = -\frac{A}{r} + B \tag{1-74}$$

For the interior of the sphere ($r < R$),

$$\frac{d}{dr}\left(r^2\frac{dV_I}{dr}\right) = -\frac{\rho r^2}{\epsilon_v} \tag{1-75}$$

Integrating,

$$r^2\frac{dV_I}{dr} = -\frac{\rho r^3}{3\epsilon_v} + C \tag{1-76}$$

or

$$\frac{dV_I}{dr} = -\frac{\rho r}{3\epsilon_v} + \frac{C}{r^2}$$

Integrating again

$$V_I = -\frac{\rho r^2}{6\epsilon_v} - \frac{C}{r} + D \tag{1-77}$$

As boundary conditions, we first use the fact that $V_E = 0$ at $r = \infty$, thus making $B = 0$. Next, we see that unless $C = 0$, we will have $V_I = \infty$ at $r = 0$. Finally, we impose the condition that V_E and V_I must have the same value $q/4\pi\epsilon_v R$ at $r = R$. Thus,

$$\frac{\rho\left(\frac{4}{3}\pi R^3\right)}{4\pi\epsilon_v R} = \frac{-\rho R^2}{6\epsilon_v} + D = \frac{-A}{R}$$

or

$$D = \frac{\rho R^2}{2\epsilon_v}, \qquad A = \frac{-\rho R^3}{3\epsilon_v}$$

and

$$V_I = \frac{\rho}{2\epsilon_v}\left(R^2 - \frac{r^2}{3}\right) \tag{1-78}$$

$$V_E = \frac{\rho R^3}{3\epsilon_v r} \tag{1-79}$$

Using

$$E = E_r = -\text{grad}_r\, V = -\frac{\partial V}{\partial r}$$

the interior and exterior fields are given by

$$E_I = \frac{\rho r}{3\epsilon_v}, \qquad E_E = \frac{\rho R^3}{3\epsilon_v r^2} \tag{1-80}$$

Plots of both E and V are shown in Fig. 1-13, and we note that the field increases linearly from the center to the surface of the sphere and then drops off again as r increases further.

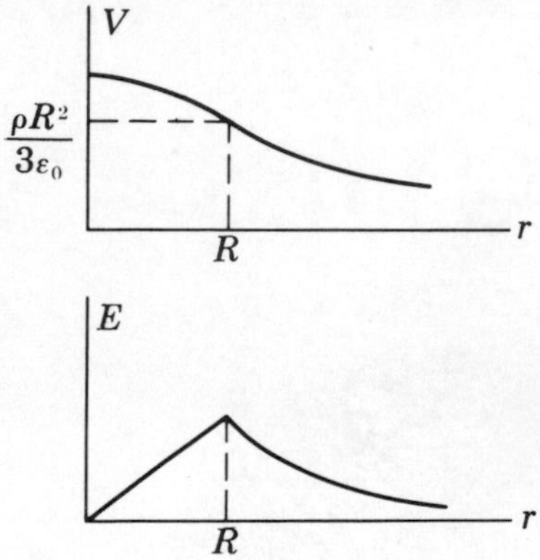

Fig. 1-13 Potential and field for a uniformly charged sphere of radius R. (From J. D. Kraus, *Electromagnetics*, McGraw-Hill Book Co., Inc., 1953, with permission.)

Problem 1-9

Find the potential inside and outside a charged spherical region of radius R having a uniform charge ρ coulombs/meter^3 by direct integration over the variable r. Your answers should agree with Eqs. (1-78) and (1-79). (*Hint:* For the exterior potential, choose a thin shell of charge inside the sphere and integrate from 0 to R. For the interior, choose a point at a a distance x from the center. The potential is the sum of that due to a sphere of radius x and a finite shell of thickness $R - x$.)

Problem 1-10

Two concentric cylinders of radii $R_1 < R_2$ have potentials V_1 and V_2. The space *between them* has a uniform charge density ρ. Find the potential V in this space.

1.7 The General Solution of Poisson's Equation

The solution to Poisson's equation (1–40) can be expressed in a more general form if we consider an arbitrary volume (Fig. 1–14) with a charge-density ρ. Choose a volume element $d\bar{V}$ surrounding a point (x, y, z), where $\bar{V}$ distinguishes volume from potential. We now wish to determine the potential at a point (x', y', z') located a distance $\bar{r}$ from (x, y, z). Considering $d\bar{V}$ to be a point-source, to a first approximation, we have

$$dV = \frac{\rho \, d\bar{V}}{4\pi\epsilon_v \bar{r}}$$

and

$$V(x', y', z') = \frac{1}{4\pi\epsilon_v} \int \frac{\rho \, d\bar{V}}{\bar{r}} \qquad \textbf{(1–81)}$$

Since V must satisfy Poisson's equation inside the charged volume, then (1–81) is the desired solution.

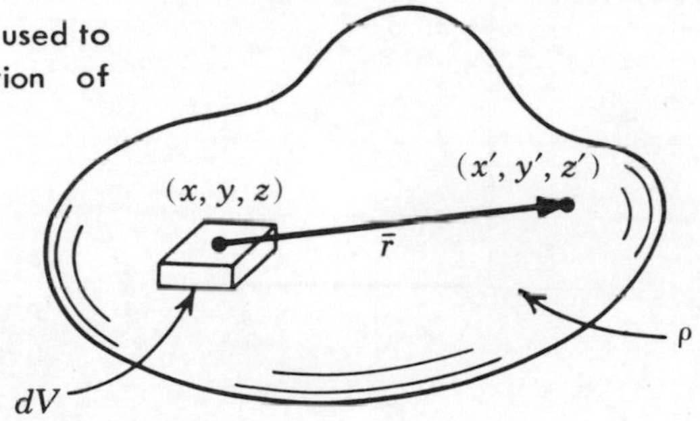

Fig. 1-14 Elementary volume used to determine the general solution of Poisson's equation.

Example 1-9 Potential for a Uniformly Charged Sphere

Consider the charged spherical region of Example 1–7. To apply (1–81) we can, without loss of generality, place (x', y', z') along the z-axis, as shown in Fig. 1–15. We then have

$$V(x', y', z') = \frac{\rho}{4\pi\epsilon_v} \int_0^R \int_0^\pi \int_0^{2\pi} \frac{r^2 \sin\theta \, d\theta \, d\phi}{\bar{r}} \qquad \textbf{(1–82)}$$

where ρ is a constant.

The variable θ can be eliminated in favor of $\bar{r}$ by using

$$\bar{r}^2 = r^2 + z'^2 - 2rz' \cos\theta \qquad \textbf{(1–83)}$$

Temporarily holding r constant, the connection between $d\bar{r}$ and $d\theta$ is obtained by differentiating (1–83), obtaining

$$\bar{r} \, d\bar{r} = rz' \sin\theta \, d\theta$$

Changing the variables also involves changing the limits. For the case $z' < r$, we see that $\bar{r}$ goes from $(r - z')$ to $(r + z')$; for $z' > $ r, the variation is from $(z' - r)$ to $(z' + r)$. Hence, (1–82) can be expressed as the sum of two integrals, as follows

$$V_I = \frac{\rho}{4\pi\epsilon_v}\left[\int_0^{z'}\int_{z'-r}^{z'+r}\int_0^{2\pi}\frac{r\,dr\,d\bar{r}\,d\phi}{z'} + \int_{z'}^{R}\int_{r-z'}^{r+z'}\int_0^{2\pi}\frac{r\,dr\,d\bar{r}\,d\phi}{z'}\right]$$

$$= \frac{\rho}{6\epsilon_v}(3R^2 - z'^2) \qquad \textbf{(1–84)}$$

in agreement with (1–78). Similarly, for the external potential,

$$V_E = \frac{\rho}{4\pi\epsilon_v}\int_0^{R}\int_{z'-r}^{z'+r}\int_0^{2\pi}\frac{r\,dr\,d\bar{r}\,d\phi}{z'} = \frac{\rho R^3}{3\epsilon_v z'} \qquad \textbf{(1–85)}$$

as previously given by (1–79).

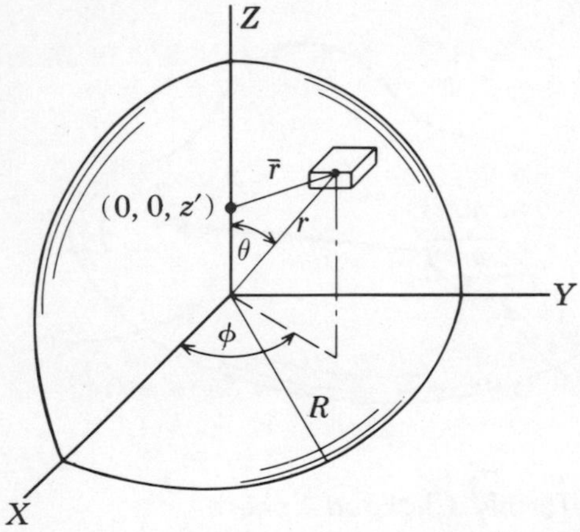

Fig. 1-15 General solution of Poisson's equation applied to a uniformly charged sphere.

1.8 Capacitance

Consider a charged body of arbitrary shape. If we wish to add further charge to this body, we must do work, because the charge already on it repels any additional charge. From the definition of potential given in Section 1.5, we then realize that this increase in charge corresponds to an increase in V, and the amount of charge, q required to produce a unit increase in V is called the *capacitance C,* or

$$C = \frac{q}{V} \qquad \textbf{(1–86)}$$

The unit of capacitance is the farad, previously defined by Eq. (1–8), so that a farad is equivalent to a coulomb/volt.

Problem 1-11

Show by dimensional analysis that the farad is the appropriate unit for capacitance.

Since calculations performed in Section 1.5 showed that electrostatic potential depends on the geometrical nature of the charges, we would expect capacitance also to depend on geometry. However, we shall now show that for a given geometry, the capacitance is a constant. For any given conductor with a surface charge σ, the potential just outside, by (1–64), is related to σ by

$$\sigma/\epsilon_v = -\frac{\partial V}{\partial r} \tag{1–87}$$

Since V satisfies Laplace's equation, so will any multiple aV of V, where a is some constant; hence, σ also increases by the same amount, and the ratio in (1–86) remains unchanged.

Consider now two bodies of arbitrary shape, having the same potential. If we transfer an amount of charge q from one to the other, one of the bodies will have an additional charge $+q$ and the other will have a deficiency $-q$. This system is said to constitute a *capacitor* whose capacitance is defined as

$$C = \frac{q}{V} \tag{1–88}$$

where V is the difference in potential established by the charge transfer. The process we have described is called *charging* the capacitor.

Example 1-10 The Spherical Capacitor

For two concentric spheres with radii R_1 and $R_2 (R_1 < R_2)$, the difference in potential was shown to be

$$V = \frac{q}{4\pi\epsilon_v}\left(\frac{1}{R_1} - \frac{1}{R_2}\right) \tag{1–37}$$

Hence,

$$C = \frac{q}{V} = \frac{4\pi\epsilon_v R_1 R_2}{R_2 - R_1} \tag{1–89}$$

Problem 1-12

Two widely separated spheres have radii a and b, respectively. If c is the separation, shows that the capacitance of the system is given by

$$C = 4\pi\epsilon_v\left[\frac{1}{a} + \frac{1}{b} - \frac{2}{c}\right]$$

Example 1-11 The Parallel-Plate Capacitor

Consider the two metal plates of Fig. 1–16, having area A and a separation d. From Eq. (1–31).

$$V = Ed = \frac{\sigma d}{\epsilon_v} = \frac{qd}{A\epsilon_v} \tag{1-90}$$

The capacitance is then

$$C = \frac{A\epsilon_v}{d} \tag{1-91}$$

From this formula, we can calculate the capacitance of a pair of metal plates with $A = 1\,\text{cm}^2$ and $d = 1\,\text{mm}$, obtaining

$$C = \frac{(10^{-2}\,\text{m})^2\, 8.85 \times 10^{-12}\,(\text{farad/m})}{(10^{-3}\,\text{m})} = \sim 1 \times 10^{-12}\text{ farad} = 1\text{ picofarad} \tag{1-92}$$

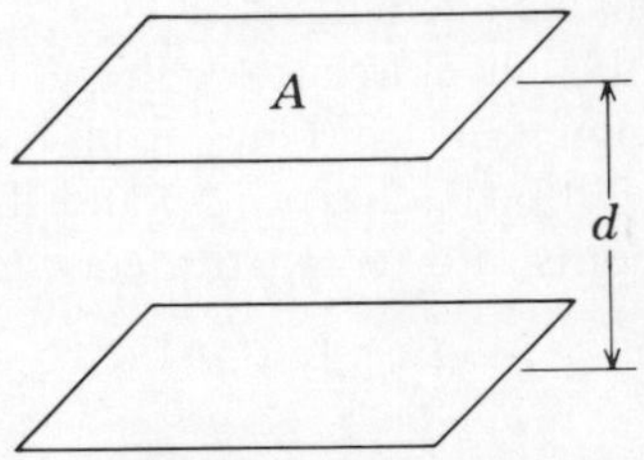

Fig. 1-16 A parallel-plate capacitor.

1.9 The Method of Images

Consider the field due to two arbitrary point-charges. If an equipotential surface surrounding one of the charges is replaced by a conductor, and if the charge is transferred to this conductor while the interior field is wiped out, then the remaining field is unaltered. This is true because the original field was governed by Laplace's equation, and the above procedure merely replaces one set of boundary conditions with another equivalent one. Similarly, the reverse procedure can be applied, and we can solve problems involving point-charges in front of conducting bodies. The charge which was eliminated is called the *image* of the other charge, and the way of using this *method of images* can be most clearly explained by the examples which follow.

Example 1-12 Image of a Point-Charge in a Grounded, Conducting Plane

Place a positive point-charge q at a distance d from the grounded, conducting plane of Fig. 1–17. The presence of the charge in front of the plane causes a redistribution of the electrons in the metal, giving it a negative surface charge which is a maximum at the point O. The creation of this surface charge is called *charging by induction*, and it results in an attractive force between the point-charge and the metal. We wish to compute this force, as well as the induced charge-density and the field at the plane.

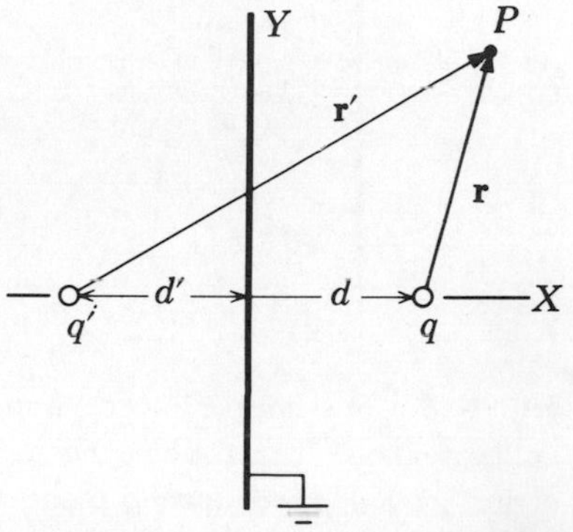

Fig. 1-17 The image of a point-charge in a grounded, conducting plane.

To solve this problem, let us place a fictitious charge q' at a distance d' behind the plane and temporarily ignore the existence of the plane. Then the potential V at some arbitrary point is

$$V = \frac{1}{4\pi\epsilon_v}\left[\frac{q}{r} + \frac{q'}{r'}\right] \tag{1–93}$$

In order to have $V = 0$ along the surface $x = 0$ (corresponding to a grounded plane), according to Eq. (1–93), we should impose the conditions

$$q' = -q, \qquad d' = d \tag{1–94}$$

Geometrically, this result corresponds to the position of the image in a plane mirror and accounts for the name of the method. Replacing the plane, we can draw the lines of force from the charge to the plane and the equipotentials (Fig. 1–18), as they are identical to the right-hand half of the corresponding diagram for two equal but opposite point-charges.

At the plane, **E** must be normal and this normal field is then (Fig. 1–19)

$$E_n = -2\left[\frac{q\cos\theta}{4\pi\epsilon_v r^2}\right] = -\left[\frac{qd}{2\pi\epsilon_v r^3}\right] \tag{1–95}$$

The surface charge-density induced on the plane may be obtained from

$$E_n = \frac{\sigma}{\epsilon_v} \tag{1–31}$$

and by (1–95)

$$\sigma = \frac{-qd}{2\pi r^3} \tag{1–96}$$

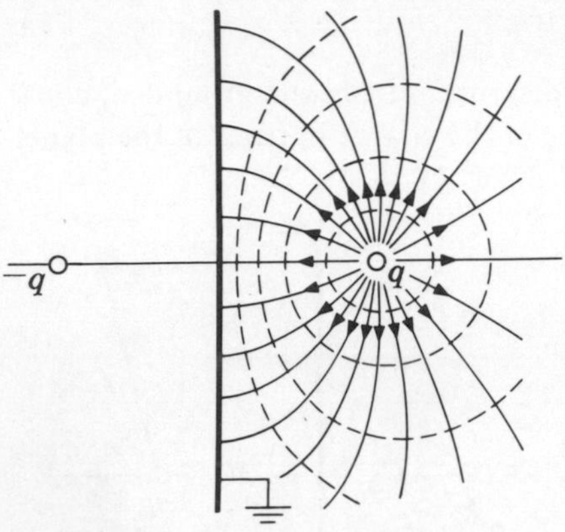

Fig. 1-18 The lines of force and equipotentials for a point-charge and a grounded, conducting plane.

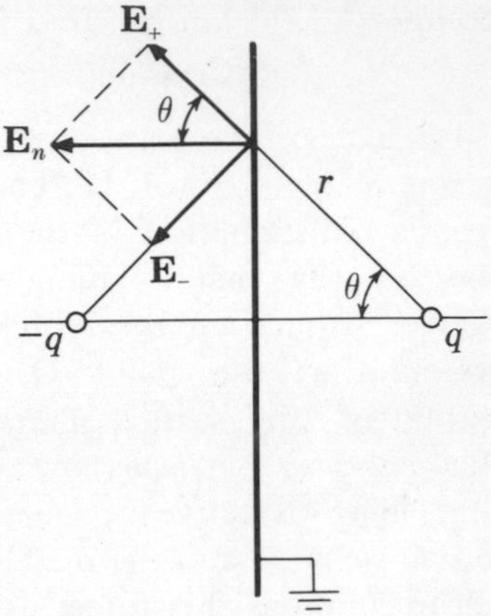

Fig. 1-19 Computation of surface charge induced on a plane by a point-charge.

This shows that the induced charge-density falls off as the cube of the distance from the plane to the position of q.

Problem 1-13

Show that the charge induced on a section of plane by a point-charge is proportional to the solid angle subtended by that section at the point-charge. (*Hint:* Use (1-95) in conjunction with the expression for a unit solid angle.)

Example 1-13 Image of a Point-Charge in a Grounded, Conducting Sphere

A charge q is placed at a distance d from the center of a grounded, conducting sphere of radius R (Fig. 1-20). Following the procedure of the previous example, we shall remove the sphere and then determine the

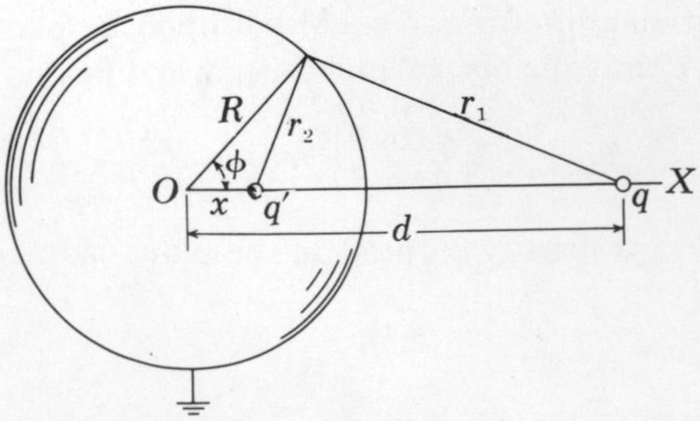

Fig. 1-20 The image of a point-charge in a grounded, conducting sphere.

magnitude q' and position x of an image charge which results in an equipotential surface corresponding to the original position of the sphere. The potential at any point a distance R from the origin is

$$V(R, \phi) = \frac{1}{4\pi\epsilon_v}\left[\frac{q}{r_1} + \frac{q'}{r_2}\right]$$

$$= \frac{1}{4\pi\epsilon_v}\left[\frac{q}{(R^2 + d^2 - 2Rd\cos\phi)^{1/2}} + \frac{q'}{(R^2 + x^2 - 2Rx\cos\phi)^{1/2}}\right]$$

To find the values of q' and x which make $V = 0$, we are facing the problem of solving a single equation with two unknowns. This equation can be written as

$$\frac{q}{[R^2 + d^2 - 2Rd\cos\phi]^{1/2}} = \frac{-q'}{[R^2 + x^2 - 2Rx\cos\phi]^{1/2}}$$

or

$$\left(\frac{q}{-q'}\right)^2 (R^2 + x^2 - 2Rx\cos\phi) = R^2 + d^2 - 2Rd\cos\phi \qquad \textbf{(1–97)}$$

Let us try the trick (which happens to work for this particular example) of assuming that the coefficients of $\cos\phi$ on each side of (1–97) must be equal, since ϕ can vary without changing R, d, or x. Hence

$$\left(\frac{q}{q'}\right)^2 x = d$$

Now if this relation is to hold, then the balance of Eq. (1 97) must be separately correct, so that

$$\left(\frac{q}{-q'}\right)^2 (R^2 + x^2) = R^2 + d^2$$

and combining these two relations gives

$$\frac{d(R^2 + x^2)}{x} = R^2 + d^2$$

or

$$dx^2 - (R^2 + d^2)x + dR^2 = 0$$

The solution of this equation is

$$x = \frac{R^2 + d^2 + \sqrt{(R^2 + d^2)^2 - 4d^2R^2}}{2d}$$

or

$$x = \frac{R^2}{d}, d \qquad \textbf{(1–98)}$$

If we substitute $x = d$ into (1–97), we see that $V = 0$ when $q = -q'$, which is a trivial solution. If we try $x = R^2/d$ in the same equation, the two sides will be identical if

$$\left(\frac{q}{-q'}\right)^2 = \frac{d^2}{R^2}$$

or

$$q = \frac{-q'd}{R} \tag{1–99}$$

Hence, the magnitude and position of the image are given by the relation

$$q' = \frac{-Rq}{d}, \qquad x = \frac{R^2}{d} \tag{1–100}$$

To find the field at the surface of the sphere, we use

$$\mathbf{E}_r = -\mathbf{grad}_r\, V$$

at $r = R$, so that

$$\mathbf{E}_r = \left.\frac{-\partial V}{\partial r}\right|_{r=R} \tag{1–101}$$

The potential at any point (r, ϕ) due to q and its image is

$$V(r, \phi) = \frac{q}{4\pi\epsilon_v}\left[\frac{1}{(r^2 + d^2 - 2rd\cos\phi)^{1/2}} - \frac{R/d}{\left(r^2 + \frac{R^4}{d^2} - \frac{2rR^2}{d}\cos\phi\right)^{1/2}}\right] \tag{1–102}$$

Differentiating (1–102) and evaluating the result at $r = R$ gives

$$E_r = \frac{q}{4\pi\epsilon_v R}\left[\frac{R^2 - d^2}{(d^2 + R^2 - 2Rd\cos\phi)^{3/2}}\right] = \frac{q(R^2 - d^2)}{4\pi\epsilon_v R r_1^3} \tag{1–103}$$

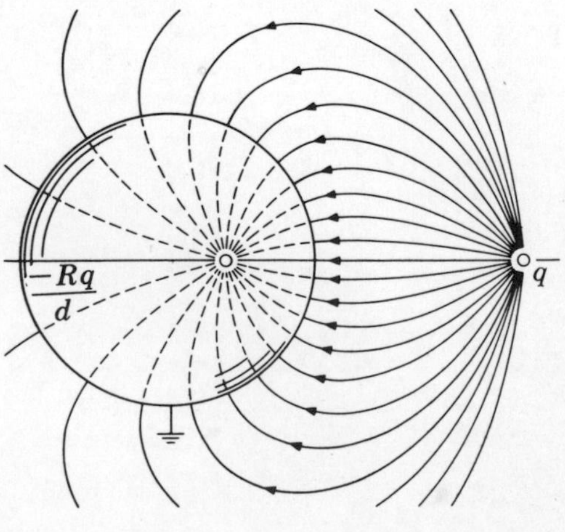

Fig. 1-21 Lines of force from a point-charge and a grounded conducting sphere. (From E. M. and E. W. Pugh, *Principles of Electricity and Magnetism*, Addison-Wesley Pub. Co., 1960, with permission.)

so that the field depends on the distance r_1 from the charge to the surface of the sphere, in accordance with an inverse-cube law. The lines of force and equipotentials for this situation are shown in Fig. 1–21.

The surface charge-density σ induced on the sphere, from (1–64), is

$$E_r = \sigma/\epsilon_v \qquad \textbf{(1–104)}$$

Combining this with (1–103) shows that

$$\sigma = \frac{-q(d^2 - R^2)}{4\pi R r_1^3} \qquad \textbf{(1–105)}$$

The force between the charge q and the sphere is

$$F = \frac{qq'}{4\pi\epsilon_v(d-x)^2} = \frac{-Rdq^2}{4\pi\epsilon_v(d^2-R^2)^2} \qquad \textbf{(1–106)}$$

Problem 1-14

A closed metal surface has the form of a quarter-sphere of radius a bounded by the xy and xz planes. A point-charge q is placed inside at a distance b from the origin, and the conductor is grounded. Make a diagram giving the location and charge on all the images you would need in order to find the potential at any point outside the conductor.

Problem 1-15

Show that Example 1-12 leads to the same results as Example 1-13, provided that we regard a plane as being equivalent to a sphere of infinite radius. (*Hint:* Let the distance from q to the closest point on the sphere be $D = d - R$, and d approach infinity in such a way that D is fixed.)

Problem 1-16

By integrating Eq. (1-105), show that the total charge induced on the sphere is $-qR/d$.

Problem 1-17

Two identical charges are placed a distance $2b$ apart. Show that a grounded sphere placed half-way between them must have a radius R approximately equal to $b/8$ to neutralize their mutual repulsion. [*Hint:* (a) Locate the images; (b) Equate the total force to zero; (c) Let $b = kR$, where $k \gg 1$; (d) Make suitable approximations.]

Example 1-14 Image of a Line-Charge in a Conducting Cylinder

To find the appropriate image for a wire having a charge λ per unit length and placed parallel to a conducting cylinder, we shall use an indirect approach. Consider two parallel wires with charges λ and $-\lambda$, respectively, a distance $2D$ apart (Fig. 1–22). The potential difference V between two points a and b in the field of the positive wire, from (1–13), is given by

$$V = \frac{\lambda}{2\pi\epsilon_v}\int_a^b \frac{dr}{r} = \frac{\lambda}{2\pi\epsilon_v} \ln \frac{b}{a} \qquad \textbf{(1–107)}$$

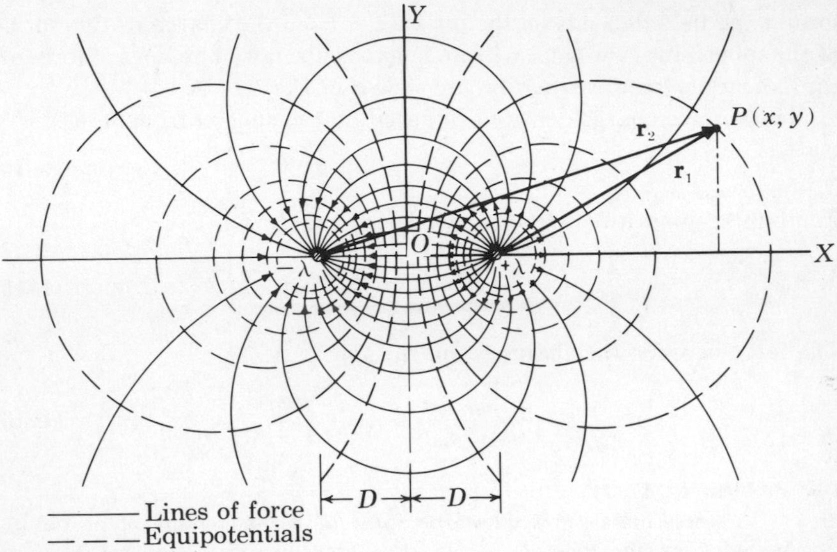

Fig. 1-22 Lines of force and equipotentials for two equal, opposite line-charges. (From Walter E. Rogers, Introduction to Electric Fields: A Vector Analysis Approach, McGraw-Hill Book Co., Inc., 1954, with permission.)

If we let $a = r_1$ and $b = D$, then the potential difference between the point P and the origin, due to the positive wire, is

$$V_+ = \frac{\lambda}{2\pi\epsilon_v} \ln \frac{D}{r_1} \tag{1–108}$$

To this, we add the corresponding quantity for the negative wire

$$V_- = \frac{\lambda}{2\pi\epsilon_v} \ln \frac{D}{r_2} \tag{1–109}$$

obtaining

$$V = V_+ + V_- = \frac{\lambda}{2\pi\epsilon_v} \ln \frac{r_2}{r_1} \tag{1–110}$$

From this equation, we note (a) that $V = 0$ along the plane $x = 0$, $y = 0$, for $r_2/r_1 = 1$, and (b) that the equipotentials are defined by

$$\frac{r_2}{r_1} = C \tag{1–111}$$

where C is a constant. This equation can be written

$$(x + D)^2 + y^2 = C^2[(x - D)^2 + y^2]$$

or

$$x^2 - 2xD\left(\frac{C^2 + 1}{C^2 - 1}\right) + D^2 + y^2 = 0 \tag{1–112}$$

Adding $D^2(C^2 + 1)^2/(C^2 - 1)^2$ to both sides completes the square and (1–112) becomes

$$\left[x - D\left(\frac{C^2 + 1}{C^2 - 1}\right)\right]^2 + y^2 = \left(\frac{2CD}{C^2 - 1}\right)^2 \tag{1–113}$$

This is the equation defining a series of circles (the dotted lines in Fig. 1–22) whose equation is

$$(x - h)^2 + y^2 = R^2 \tag{1–114}$$

where the centers of these circles lie on the x-axis at a distance from the origin

$$h = D\left(\frac{C^2 + 1}{C^2 - 1}\right) \tag{1–115}$$

and the radii are given by

$$R = \frac{2CD}{|C^2 - 1|} \tag{1–116}$$

Note that h can be positive or negative, depending on whether C is greater or less than unity. For each $C > 1$, there is a corresponding circle on the other side of the y-axis specified by $C' = 1/C$. Figure 1–22 also shows the lines of force (the solid lines), and these are another family of circles which meet the equipotentials at right angles.

We can now introduce the method of images by realizing that the charge $-\lambda$ can be transferred to any of the cylinders surrounding this wire and the internal field wiped out. Then $-\lambda$ is the image that would be needed for the reverse process. To find the positions of λ, $-\lambda$, and the cylinder, consider Fig. 1–23.

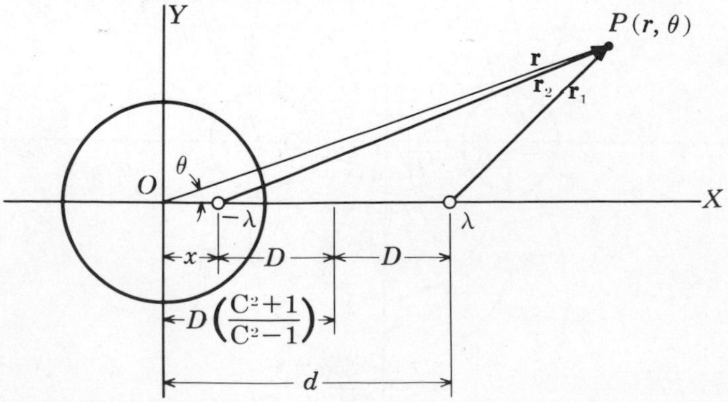

Fig. 1-23 Image of a line-charge in a conducting cylinder.

Then
$$x = D\left(\frac{C^2+1}{C^2-1}\right) - D = \frac{2D}{C^2-1}$$

and
$$xd = x(x+2D) = \frac{2D}{C^2-1}\left(\frac{2DC^2}{C^2-1}\right) = \frac{4D^2C^2}{(C^2-1)^2}$$

which, by (1–116), becomes
$$xd = R^2$$

This is identical to Eq. (1–100) obtained for the sphere. In this case, however, the image charge has the same magnitude as the original charge, in contrast to the point-charge and sphere.

Problem 1-18

Two uniformly and oppositely charged wires run through a metal cylinder of radius R. Show that there will be no force between them if they have a separation of $2R\sqrt{\sqrt{5}-2}$. (*Hint:* Consider the force on one wire due to the other wire and to both of the images.)

Example 1-15 Two-Conductor Transmission Line

The results of the previous example can be applied to a transmission line composed of two parallel conducting cylinders of radius R (Fig. 1–24).

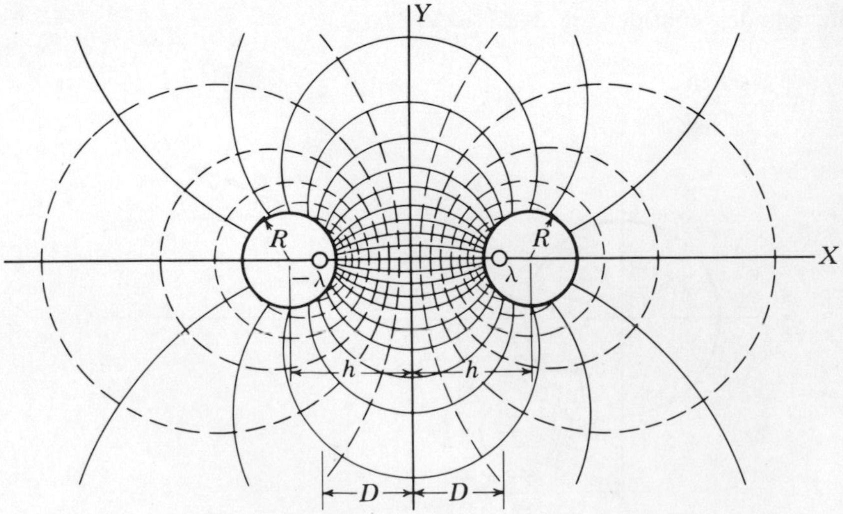

Fig. 1-24 Lines of force and equipotentials for two conducting cylinders.

The charges $\pm\lambda$ on the wires are transferred to the cylinders, which attract one another with a force per unit length given by

$$F_l = \frac{\lambda^2}{4\pi\epsilon_v D} \tag{1-117}$$

This expression comes from (1–14), using $2D$ as the distance between the image line-charges. The potential difference between the surface of the positive cylinder and the origin due to both image charges is

$$V = \frac{\lambda}{2\pi\epsilon_v}\ln C \tag{1-118}$$

from (1–110) and (1–111). The value of C to use in this is obtained by eliminating D from (1–115) and (1–116), giving

$$\frac{h}{R} = \frac{C^2+1}{2C}$$

or

$$C = \frac{h \pm \sqrt{h^2 - R^2}}{R} \tag{1-119}$$

The two values of C are then

$$\begin{aligned} C_1 &= \frac{h + \sqrt{h^2 - R^2}}{R} \\ C_2 &= \frac{h - \sqrt{h^2 - R^2}}{R} \end{aligned} \tag{1-120}$$

and we note that

$$C_1 C_2 = 1 \qquad \text{or} \qquad C_1 = 1/C_2$$

as we have already discussed. Hence, the potential difference between the surfaces of the two cylinders is

$$\begin{aligned} V = V_1 - V_2 &= \frac{\lambda}{2\pi\epsilon_v}\ln C_1 - \frac{\lambda}{2\pi\epsilon_v}\ln C_2 \\ &= \frac{\lambda}{2\pi\epsilon_v}\ln\left[\frac{h + \sqrt{h^2 - R^2}}{h - \sqrt{h^2 - R^2}}\right] \end{aligned} \tag{1-121}$$

Returning to the line-charge and its image in a cylinder, the field is obtained from (1–110) and Fig. 1–25. We see that

$$\begin{aligned} r_1^2 &= r^2 + d^2 - 2rd\cos\theta \\ r_2^2 &= r^2 + x^2 - 2rx\cos\theta \\ &= r^2 + \frac{R^4}{d^2} - \frac{2rR^2}{d}\cos\theta \end{aligned} \tag{1-122}$$

Using $\mathbf{E} = -\mathbf{grad}\, V$

or

$$E_r = -\frac{\partial V}{\partial r}$$

and carrying out the differentiation,

$$E_r = \frac{-\lambda}{2\pi\epsilon_v}\left[\frac{r - d\cos\theta}{r_1^2} - \frac{r - \frac{R^2}{d}\cos\theta}{r_2^2}\right] \tag{1-123}$$

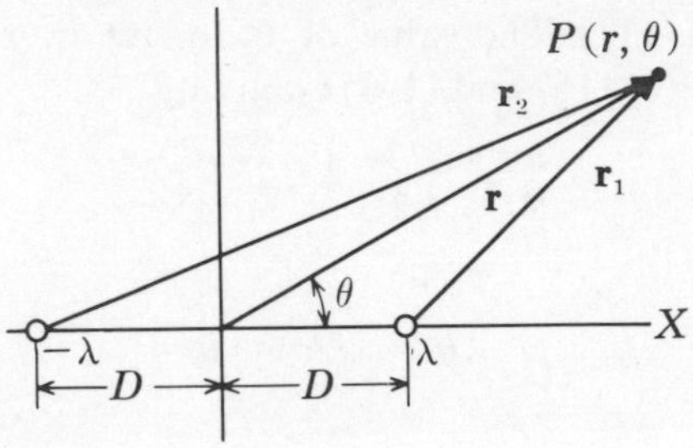

Fig. 1-25 Calculation of surface charge induced on a cylinder by a line-charge.

At $r = R$, this becomes

$$E_r = \frac{-\lambda}{2\pi\epsilon_v}\left[\frac{R - \frac{d^2}{R}}{R^2 + d^2 - 2Rd\cos\theta}\right] \tag{1-124}$$

To find the charge induced on a cylinder by a parallel line-charge λ, we use the procedure that led to Eq. (1–105), obtaining

$$\sigma = \frac{-\lambda}{2\pi}\left[\frac{R - \frac{d^2}{R}}{R^2 + d^2 - 2Rd\cos\theta}\right] \tag{1-125}$$

Problem 1-19

A telegraph wire of radius a having a uniform charge λ per unit length runs at a height h above the earth, where $h \gg a$. Find the force and the potential difference between the wire and the earth. Sketch the lines of force and equipotentials.

1.10 Electrostatic Energy

Consider a group of n charges $q_1, q_2, \ldots, q_n$, which are originally all far apart. First, let us bring q_2 up to a distance r_{12} from q_1. The work W_2 done in this process is

$$W_2 = Vq_2 = \frac{q_1 q_2}{4\pi\epsilon_v r_{12}} \tag{1–126}$$

from Eq. (1–38). Next, bring q_3 up to a distance r_{13} from q_1 and r_{23} from q_2, doing an amount of work

$$W_3 = \frac{1}{4\pi\epsilon_v}\left[\frac{q_1 q_3}{r_{13}} + \frac{q_2 q_3}{r_{23}}\right] \tag{1–127}$$

Carrying on in this fashion for all the remaining charges, and adding the expressions of the form (1–126) and (1–127), the total work done is

$$2W = \frac{1}{4\pi\epsilon_v}\left[q_1\left(\frac{q_2}{r_{12}} + \frac{q_3}{r_{13}} + \frac{q_4}{r_{14}} + \cdots\right)\right.$$
$$\left. + q_2\left(\frac{q_1}{r_{21}} + \frac{q_3}{r_{23}} + \frac{q_4}{r_{24}} + \cdots\right) + \cdots + q_n\left(\frac{q_1}{r_{n1}} + \cdots + \frac{q_{n-1}}{r_{n(n-1)}}\right)\right] \tag{1–128}$$

Each term in parentheses, when divided by $4\pi\epsilon_v$, represents the potential V_i of any one charge, q_i, in the field of all the other $(n - 1)$ charges, and the factor of 2 appears because each term in the sum occurs twice. Hence, (1–128) can be written

$$W = \tfrac{1}{2}\, \Sigma q_i V_i \tag{1–129}$$

and this is the electrostatic potential energy for the group of charges in their mutual field. Note that in arriving at (1–129), we did *not* consider the self-energy, that is, the amount of energy required to place each of the charges q_i on the corresponding body.

For a continuous distribution with charge-density ρ, we wish to show that the expression corresponding to (1–129) is

$$W = \tfrac{1}{2}\int \rho V d\bar{V} \tag{1–130}$$

where we use $\bar{V}$ to distinquish volume from potential V. We do this in a fashion like that already used: Start with the charge-density equal to zero and build it up to the final value ρ. At any stage during the process, the charge-density will then be $\alpha\rho$, where α is a number between 0 and 1. If $\alpha\rho$ is the density at some point, the corresponding charge in a volume element $d\bar{V}$ at this point is

$$dq' = \alpha\rho\, d\bar{V}$$

and the potential V' is

$$V' = \alpha V$$

where V is the final potential at this point. If we increase α to $\alpha + d\alpha$, the change in the charge is

$$dq = \rho\, dVd\alpha$$

and the increase in energy is

$$dW = V'dq = (\alpha V)(\rho\, d\bar{V} d\alpha)$$

Then

$$W = \int_0^1 \alpha\, d\alpha \int \rho V d\bar{V} = \frac{1}{2}\int \rho V d\bar{V}$$

as we wished to show. In this calculation, the self-energies have been included.

If we now substitute (1–39) into (1–130), we obtain

$$W = \frac{\epsilon_v}{2}\int V \operatorname{div} \mathbf{E}\, d\bar{V}$$

and the vector identity (A–3) converts this into

$$W = \frac{\epsilon_v}{2}\int\left[\operatorname{div}(V\mathbf{E}) - \mathbf{E}\cdot\mathbf{grad}\, V\right]d\bar{V}$$

Then, by the divergence theorem (A–11), we obtain

$$W = \frac{\epsilon_v}{2}\left[\int V\mathbf{E}\cdot d\mathbf{A} - \int \mathbf{E}\cdot\mathbf{grad} V d\bar{V}\right] \tag{1–131}$$

In choosing a Gaussian surface A over which to perform the integration, we are free to make it any size we please, provided that it surrounds all the charge ρ in our distribution. Let us make A very large. On such a surface, A is proportional to r^2. In addition, if we make this surface large enough so that all of the charges we are concerned with can be regarded as point-charges, then E is proportional to $1/r^2$ and V is proportional to $1/r$, where r is the distance to the distribution. Hence, the product of the three terms in the first integral of Eq. (1–131) depends upon $1/r$, and becomes vanishingly small for a large r.

The second integral is transformed by the relation

$$\mathbf{E} = -\,\mathbf{grad}\, V \tag{1–36}$$

and we obtain finally

$$W = \frac{\epsilon_v}{2}\int E^2 dV \tag{1–132}$$

This shows that the *energy density* E_V, or energy per unit volume, associated with an electric field is

$$E_V = \frac{dW}{dV} = \frac{\epsilon_v}{2}E^2 \tag{1–133}$$

Example 1-16 Energy Required to Charge a Capacitor

The energy required to charge a capacitor, as obtained by applying (1–129) to a system of of only two bodies, is

$$W = \frac{1}{2}qV \tag{1–134}$$

To express W in terms of the capacitance, we use

$$q = VC \tag{1–86}$$

obtaining

$$W = \frac{1}{2}CV^2 \tag{1–135}$$

Problem 1-20

Consider an isolated, uniformly charged sphere of radius R. Verify (1-135) for this body. (*Hint:* Find W from (1-132) by integrating over all the space external to the sphere.)

2 Electrostatic Fields in Dielectrics

2.1 Introduction

In this chapter, we wish to consider the nature of electric fields in regions containing matter. In discussing the field due to a charged metal plate in Chapter 1, it was pointed out that all of the charge resides on the surface and that the internal field vanishes. This is true in general for the class of materials known as *conductors*. Conductors permit the free motion of electric charge, whereas *insulators* or *dielectrics* do not. We are going to discuss the electrical properties of dielectrics from what is known as a *macroscopic* or large-scale viewpoint. That is, we shall consider the relation among the forces, fields, and charges without offering an atomic or *microscopic* theory to explain any of these relationships. Before presenting the theory of fields in material media, however, we should consider one further topic from vacuum electrostatics, and this is given in the next section.

2.2 Dipoles

A *dipole* is defined as a pair of equal, but opposite, point-charges which are arbitrarily close. That is, the separation a of $+q$ and $-p$ in Fig. 2–1 obeys the condition

$$a \rightarrow 0 \qquad \text{(2–1)}$$

We see from the figure that the absolute potential V at the point P is

$$V = \frac{q}{4\pi\epsilon_v}\left[\frac{1}{r_1} - \frac{1}{r_2}\right] \qquad \text{(2–2)}$$

where

$$r_1^2 = r^2 + \left(\frac{a}{2}\right)^2 - ar\, cos\, \theta \qquad \text{(2–3)}$$

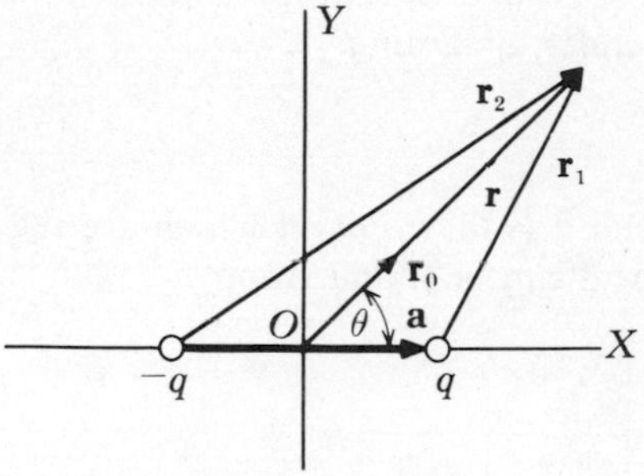

Fig. 2-1 A dipole.

Dividing through by r^2 gives

$$\left(\frac{r_1}{r}\right)^2 = 1 + \left(\frac{a}{2r}\right)^2 - \frac{a}{r}\cos\theta$$

Solving this for r/r_1 and using the binomial theorem, we obtain

$$\frac{r}{r_1} = \left\{1 + \left[\left(\frac{a}{2r}\right)^2 - \frac{a}{r}\cos\theta\right]\right\}^{-1/2}$$

$$= 1 - \frac{1}{2}\left(\frac{a^2}{4r^2} - \frac{a}{r}\cos\theta\right) + \frac{\left(-\frac{1}{2}\right)\left(-\frac{3}{2}\right)}{2!}\left(\frac{a^2}{4r^2} - \frac{a}{r}\cos\theta\right)^2 + \cdots$$

We can now neglect terms smaller than $(a/r)^2$, since $a \ll r$, and get

$$\frac{r}{r_1} = 1 + \frac{a}{2r}\cos\theta + \left(\frac{a^2}{4r^2}\right)\frac{3\cos^2\theta - 1}{2} \qquad \text{(2–4)}$$

Similarly, the ratio r/r_2 can be expressed as

$$\frac{r}{r_2} = 1 - \frac{a}{2r}\cos\theta + \left(\frac{a^2}{4r^2}\right)\frac{3\cos^2\theta - 1}{2} \qquad \text{(2–5)}$$

so that (2–2) becomes

$$V = \frac{qa\cos\theta}{4\pi\epsilon_v r^2} \qquad \text{(2–6)}$$

If we now define the *dipole moment* $\mathbf{p}$ as

$$\mathbf{p} = q\mathbf{a} \qquad \text{(2–7)}$$

where $\mathbf{a}$ is a vector directed from $-q$ to q, (2–6) can be written in the alternate form

$$V = \frac{\mathbf{p}\cdot\mathbf{r}_0}{4\pi\epsilon_v r^2} \qquad \text{(2–8)}$$

where $\mathbf{r}_0$ is a unit vector along $\mathbf{r}$. We note that Eq. (2–6) shows that the potential falls off as the square of the distance, whereas it decreases as the first power for a single point-charge. We can think of this as being due to the fact that the two charges in the dipole appear almost as one at a long distance; hence, their fields nearly cancel, thus causing V to decrease more rapidly with r than it would for a single point-charge.

To find the equipotentials, we let V in (2–6) assume a series of constant values, obtaining

$$\frac{\cos\theta}{r^2} = C \tag{2–9}$$

and it is these curves which are the dotted lines of Fig. 2–2. The electric field can be found from

$$E = -\mathbf{grad}\, V \tag{1–36}$$

or

$$E_r = -\frac{\partial V}{\partial r} = \frac{qa\cos\theta}{2\pi\epsilon_v r^3}$$
$$E_\theta = -\frac{1}{r}\frac{\partial V}{\partial \theta} = \frac{qa\sin\theta}{4\pi\epsilon_v r^3} \tag{2–10}$$

showing that E falls off as the inverse cube of r. The field lines, or lines of force, are shown as solid lines in the figure.

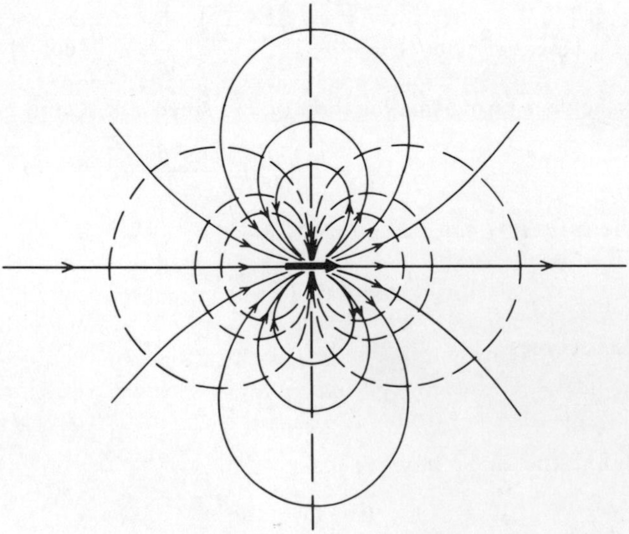

Fig. 2-2 The lines of force and equipotentials for a dipole. (From A.R. von Hippel, Dielectrics and Waves, John Wiley & Sons, Inc., 1954, with permission.)

2.3 Polarized Dielectrics

We are now ready to discuss what happens when we take a sample of dielectric material and place it in an electric field **E**. Although we are not going to make any assumptions about the atomic or electronic structure of the material, we do have to assume that it is composed of a large number of pairs of equal, but opposite, point-charges, and that both charges of each pair occupy the same point, so that the material is originally neutral. The application of the electric field then causes all the positive charges to move along the direction of the field and all the negative charges to move in the opposite direction; thus, the material now contains a large number of dipoles. The transition from the pure neutral to the dipole condition is illustrated in Fig. 2–3 in a highly schematic way. In order to describe the situation shown by Fig. 2–3 in a quantitative fashion, we define the *polarization* **P** of the material as the dipole moment **p** per unit volume. Since the dipole moment may vary from one region to another, the definition of the polarization is expressed as a derivative, or

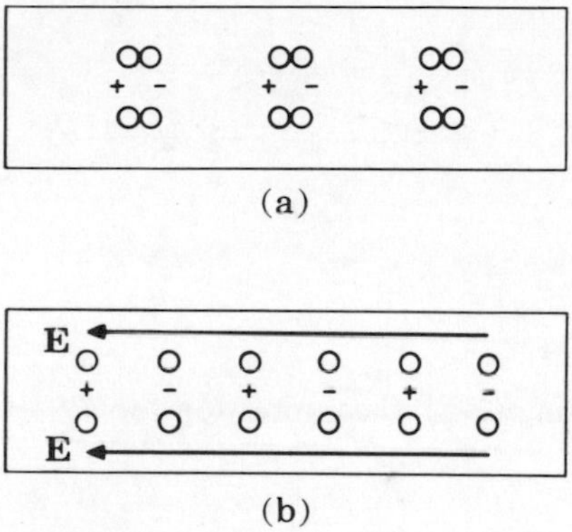

Fig. 2-3 (a) The charges in a neutral dielectric. (b) The charge separation produced by an applied electric field.

$$\mathbf{P} = \frac{d\mathbf{p}}{d\bar{V}} \tag{2–11}$$

Now we would like to calculate the relations between the polarization **P** and the more familiar quantities, such as the charge and the field. To do this, consider the dielectric region shown in Fig. 2–4. This volume $\bar{V}$ is polarized, and the polarization is non-uniform, as indicated by arrows, which represent dipole moments of various strengths and directions. Inside the dielectric region, we choose a volume element $d\bar{V}$ surrounding an arbitrary point whose position-vector is denoted **r**, where

$$\mathbf{r} = x\mathbf{i} + y\mathbf{j} + z\mathbf{k} \tag{2–12}$$

We would like to calculate the potential dV at the point whose position-vector is $\mathbf{r}'$, where

$$\mathbf{r}' = x'\mathbf{i} + y'\mathbf{j} + z'\mathbf{k} \tag{2–13}$$

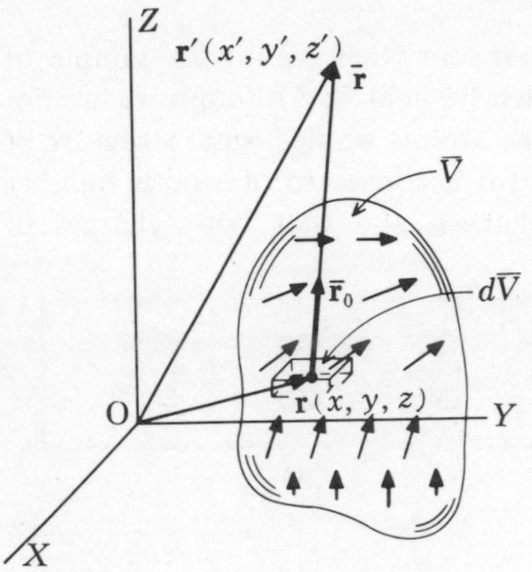

Fig. 2-4 Calculation of equivalent surface and volume charges.

Using (2–8), the expression for dV is

$$dV = \frac{d\mathbf{p}\cdot\bar{\mathbf{r}}_0}{4\pi\epsilon_v\bar{\mathbf{r}}^2} \tag{2–14}$$

where $d\mathbf{p}$ is the dipole moment of the element $d\bar{V}$, $\bar{\mathbf{r}}$ is the vector joining the points (x, y, z) and (x', y', z'), and $\bar{\mathbf{r}}_0$ is a unit vector along $\bar{\mathbf{r}}$. By (2–11), this quantity is

$$d\mathbf{p} = \mathbf{P}\, d\bar{V} \tag{2–15}$$

so that (2–14) becomes

$$dV = \frac{\mathbf{P}\cdot\bar{\mathbf{r}}_0\, d\bar{V}}{4\pi\epsilon_v\bar{r}^2} \tag{2–16}$$

The right-hand side of (2–16) can be converted, using a vector identity to be developed in the following problem.

Problem 2-1
Using

$$\bar{\mathbf{r}} = \mathbf{r}' - \mathbf{r} \tag{2-17}$$

or

$$\bar{r} = [(x' - x)^2 + (y' - y)^2 + (z' - z)^2]^{1/2} \tag{2-18}$$

show that

$$\mathbf{grad}\left(\frac{1}{\bar{r}}\right) = \frac{\bar{\mathbf{r}}}{\bar{r}^3} \tag{2-19}$$

and

$$\mathbf{grad}'\left(\frac{1}{\bar{r}}\right) = -\frac{\bar{\mathbf{r}}}{\bar{r}^3} \tag{2-20}$$

where

$$\begin{aligned} \mathbf{grad} &= \mathbf{i}\frac{\partial}{\partial x} + \mathbf{j}\frac{\partial}{\partial y} + \mathbf{k}\frac{\partial}{\partial z} \\ \mathbf{grad}' &= \mathbf{i}\frac{\partial}{\partial x'} + \mathbf{j}\frac{\partial}{\partial y'} + \mathbf{k}\frac{\partial}{\partial z'} \end{aligned} \tag{2-21}$$

The operator **grad** is said to be taken with respect to the *source point* (x, y, z), and the operator **grad**$'$ is expressed in terms of the *field point* (x', y', z').

Applying (2–19) to (2–16), we obtain

$$dV = \frac{\mathbf{P}\cdot\mathbf{grad}\left(\frac{1}{\bar{r}}\right) d\bar{V}}{4\pi\epsilon_v}$$

or

$$V = \frac{1}{4\pi\epsilon_v}\int \mathbf{P}\cdot\mathbf{grad}\left(\frac{1}{\bar{r}}\right) d\bar{V} \tag{2-22}$$

This expression can be further transformed by using the identity (A–3), which shows that

$$\mathbf{P}\cdot\mathbf{grad}\left(\frac{1}{\bar{r}}\right) = \mathrm{div}\left(\frac{\mathbf{P}}{\bar{r}}\right) - \frac{\mathrm{div}\,\mathbf{P}}{\bar{r}} \tag{2-23}$$

Equation (2–22) then becomes

$$V = \frac{1}{4\pi\epsilon_v}\int\left[\mathrm{div}\left(\frac{\mathbf{P}}{r}\right) - \frac{\mathrm{div}\,\mathbf{P}}{\bar{r}}\right] d\bar{V} \tag{2-24}$$

If we now apply the divergence theorem (A–11) to the first term on the right, we obtain

$$V = \frac{1}{4\pi\epsilon_v}\oint\frac{\mathbf{P}\cdot d\mathbf{A}}{\bar{r}} - \frac{1}{4\pi\epsilon_v}\int\frac{\mathrm{div}\,\mathbf{P}}{\bar{r}}\, d\bar{V} \tag{2-25}$$

This equation tells us that the potential V at the point $\mathbf{r}'$ is the sum of two contributions: a surface term and a volume term, both of which are due to the polarization of the dielectric medium. Further, from the general solution (1–81) of Poisson's equation, we see that the potential due to the volume V can be regarded as originating from a surface charge-density σ' and a volume charge-density ρ', with V being given by

$$V = \frac{1}{4\pi\epsilon_v}\left[\oint\frac{\sigma'\, dA}{\bar{r}} + \int\frac{\rho'\, d\bar{V}}{\bar{r}}\right] \tag{2-26}$$

Comparing (2–25) and (2–26) gives

$$\sigma' = P_n, \qquad \rho' = -\mathrm{div}\,\mathbf{P} \tag{2-27}$$

where the primes are used to emphasize the fact that σ' and ρ' represent *bound* charges. They are charge-densities created by the separations of the pairs of charge mentioned above (for example, they might be the electrons and nuclei of the material). The material may also have electrons or ions which are free to conduct, but these do not form part of σ' or ρ'.

Returning to Gauss' law, Eq. (1–22), the total charge-density must include both the free charge-density ρ and the bound charge-density ρ', so that we have

$$\operatorname{div} \mathbf{E} = \frac{\rho + \rho'}{\epsilon_v}$$

Using (2–27), this becomes

$$\operatorname{div} \mathbf{E} = \frac{(\rho - \operatorname{div} \mathbf{P})}{\epsilon_v}$$

or

$$\operatorname{div} (\epsilon_v \mathbf{E} + \mathbf{P}) = \rho \tag{2–28}$$

The quantity in parentheses is called the *electric displacement* or *dielectric flux density* **D**, so that

$$\mathbf{D} = \epsilon_v \mathbf{E} + \mathbf{P} \tag{2–29}$$

We note that for an unpolarized medium ($\mathbf{P} = 0$), this definition reduces to

$$\mathbf{D} = \epsilon_v \mathbf{E} \tag{2–30}$$

which is the form previously encountered as Eq. (1–24). Using (2–29) in (2–28) gives

$$\operatorname{div} \mathbf{D} = \rho \tag{2–31}$$

as the most general form of the first Maxwell equation (1–39). It should be kept in mind that ρ on the right-hand side of (2–31) refers to the free charge in the medium.

Let us now assume that the dipole moment induced in a dielectric by an external field **E** is directly proportional to **E**. Such materials are said to be *linear*. We shall also require the electrical properties of the dielectric to be independent of direction, and this condition defines an *isotropic* material. Finally, if the material is also homogeneous, then it is said to be a *Class A* dielectric. For such materials

$$\mathbf{P} \propto \mathbf{E}$$

and we shall write this in the form

$$\mathbf{P} = \epsilon_v \eta \mathbf{E} \tag{2–32}$$

where the proportionality constant η is called the *electric susceptibility*, and the factor ϵ_v is used to make η a dimensionless quantity. Then (2–29) becomes

$$\mathbf{D} = \epsilon_v (1 + \eta) \mathbf{E} \tag{2–33}$$

The quantity $(1 + \eta)$ in (2–36) is called the *relative dielectric coefficient* ϵ_r of the medium, so that

$$\epsilon_r = (1 + \eta) \tag{2–34}$$

and (2–33) may then be written

$$\mathbf{D} = \epsilon_r \epsilon_v \mathbf{E} \tag{2–35}$$

Comparing this relation with Eq. (2–30), we see that the presence of the dielectric affects the ratio of **D** to **E** by a factor of ϵ_r. The physical significance of this result will be discussed in Example 2–1 below.

Example 2-1 Gauss' Law in a Dielectric

Gauss' law for a dielectric can be derived directly from the original form given by Eq. (1–22). We construct an arbitrary closed surface inside a polarized dielectric also containing some free charge q (Fig. 2–5). The right-hand side of Eq. (1–22) must include all the charges enclosed by the Gaussian surface, so that it becomes

$$\oint \mathbf{E}\cdot d\mathbf{A} = \frac{q + q'}{\epsilon_v} \tag{2–36}$$

where q is the free charge and q' is the bound charge. The bound charge enclosed by the Gaussian surface, from (2–27), is

$$q' = \oint_{\bar{A}} \mathbf{P}\cdot d\mathbf{A} + \int (-\operatorname{div} \mathbf{P})\, d\bar{V} \tag{2–37}$$

where $\bar{A}$ denotes the surface of the free charge inside the dielectric. Note that the surface integral in (2–37) contains no contribution from A, since this surface lies entirely within the dielectric and there is no surface polarization charge in the interior; that is, $\sigma' = 0$ over A. If we apply the divergence theorem (A–11) to the second integral on the right of (2–37), we obtain

$$\int \operatorname{div} \mathbf{P}\, d\bar{V} = \oint_{\bar{A}} \mathbf{P}\cdot d\mathbf{A} + \oint_{A} \mathbf{P}\cdot d\mathbf{A}$$

so that (2–37) becomes

$$q' = -\oint_{A} \mathbf{P}\cdot d\mathbf{A}$$

Combining this with (2–36) gives

$$\oint_{A} (\epsilon_v \mathbf{E} + \mathbf{P})\cdot d\mathbf{A} = q$$

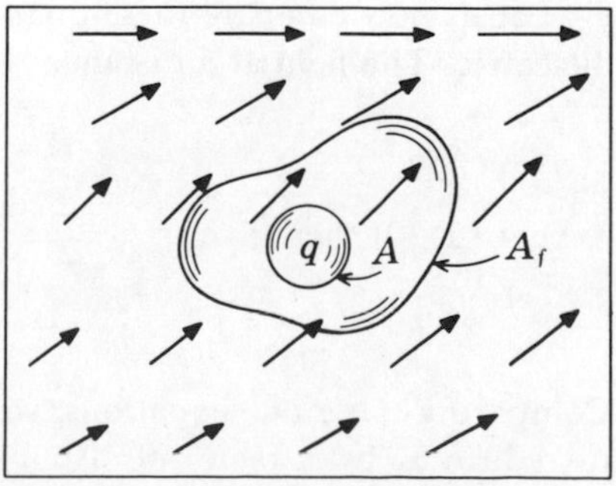

Fig. 2-5 Application of Gauss' law to a dielectric.

and by (2–29), we obtain

$$\oint \mathbf{D} \cdot d\mathbf{A} = q \tag{2–38}$$

Again using the divergence theorem, we can convert this into

$$\operatorname{div} \mathbf{D} = \rho$$

agreeing with Eq. (2–31).

Example 2-2 Point-Charge in a Dielectric Medium

Let us consider a point-charge q immersed in a Class A dielectric fluid with a dielectric coefficient ϵ_r. As was the case for a vacuum, the field **E** is symmetrical with respect to q. In addition, **D** and **P** have the same symmetry, since (2–29) shows they are colinear with **E**. Gauss' law (2–38) then becomes

$$D(4\pi r^2) = q$$

or

$$D = \frac{q}{4\pi r^2} \tag{2–39}$$

This may also be written in vector form as

$$\mathbf{D} = \frac{q}{4\pi r^2}\mathbf{r}_0 \tag{2–40}$$

where $\mathbf{r}_0$ is a unit vector along the radius. By (2–35), the field becomes

$$\mathbf{E} = \frac{1}{\epsilon_r \epsilon_v}\frac{q}{4\pi r^2}\mathbf{r}_0 \tag{2–41}$$

and the polarization, from (2–29) is

$$\mathbf{P} = \frac{(\epsilon_r - 1)}{4\pi\epsilon_r r^2}\mathbf{r}_0 \tag{2–42}$$

Let us now compare these quantities in the presence and absence of a dielectric. The field at a distance r from a point-charge in a vacuum is

$$\mathbf{E} = \frac{q}{4\pi\epsilon_v r^2}\mathbf{r}_0 \tag{1–12}$$

so that (2–30) then gives

$$\mathbf{D} = \frac{q}{4\pi r^2}\mathbf{r}_0 \tag{2–43}$$

Comparing these two equations, we see that the effect of the dielectric is to reduce **E** by a factor of ϵ_r but to leave **D** unchanged. If we assume for convenience that the point-charge is at the center of a dielectric sphere, then the behavior of **E** and **D** are illustrated by Fig. 2–6. The lines of constant thickness in Fig. 2–6 indicate that **D** is continuous across the

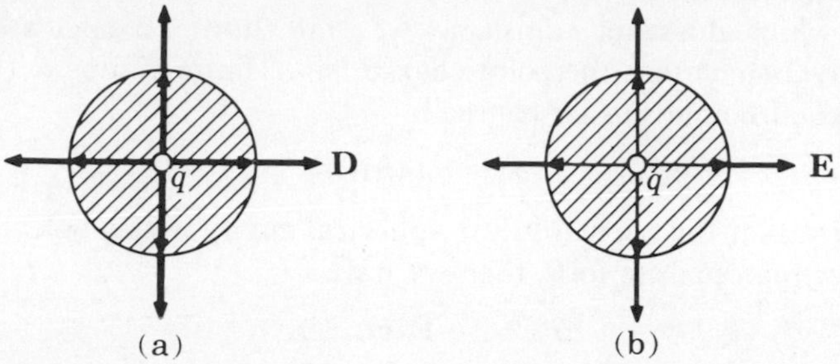

Fig. 2-6 Electric field and electric displacement inside a dielectric.

surface of the sphere, whereas the abrupt change in the value of **E** is denoted by the corresponding change in thickness.

The reason for this discontinuity in **E** can be found by considering the effect of the polarization of the sphere. In Fig. 2–7, we show the central charge and the induced dipoles, which are radial with respect to q. The field due to q is shown in Fig. 2–6a, and the field of the dipoles is opposite in sign and opposes the field of q. This results in the reduction of the resultant field that we have calculated.

We can express this effect quantitatively in another way through Eq. (2–27). First, we notice that

$$\rho' = -\operatorname{div} \mathbf{P} = 0 \qquad \textbf{(2–44)}$$

where we have used the expression (A–19) for the divergence in spherical coordinates. Figure 2–7 indicates schematically how dipoles can be arranged radially in a way that will cause the internal charges to cancel one another and the bound volume-charge vanishes. On the other hand, there is a

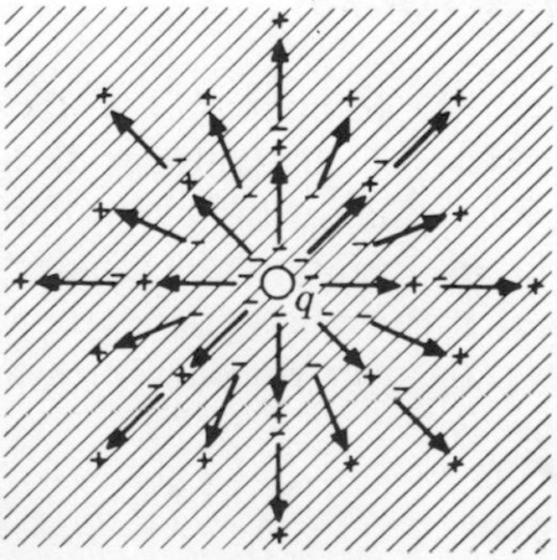

Fig. 2-7 Induced dipoles around a point-charge in a dielectric medium.

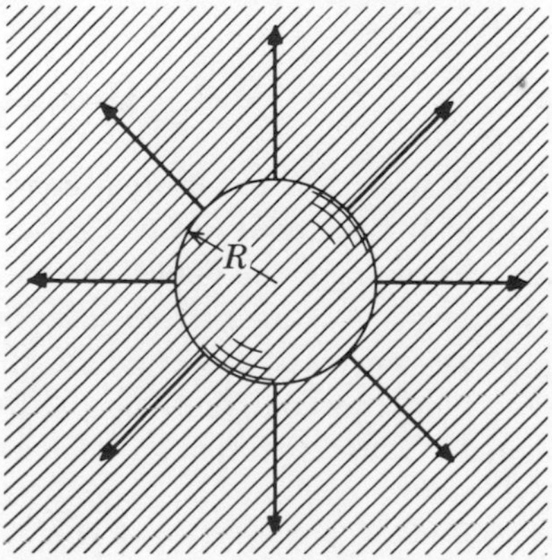

Fig. 2-8 A charge of radius R in a dielectric.

bound surface-charge ρ' on the interface between the point-charge and the dielectric which does not vanish, as we shall show. To calculate ρ' let us temporarily assume that the point-charge has a finite radius R (Fig. 2–8). Then the total bound surface-charge is

$$q' = \sigma'(4\pi R^2) \tag{2–45}$$

If we realize that the normal to the spherical cavity in the dielectric points in the direction opposite to **P**, then we have

$$P_n = -\mathbf{P}\cdot\mathbf{r}_0 = \sigma' \tag{2–46}$$

and (2–45) becomes

$$q' = -\frac{(\epsilon_r - 1)q}{\epsilon_r} \tag{2–47}$$

using (2–42) for $r = R$. Since the radius R cancels out during this calculation, (2–47) is still valid as R approaches zero as a limit. The total charge existing at the site of the point-charge is then

$$q' + q = \frac{q}{\epsilon_r} \tag{2–48}$$

which explains why the field we observe at other points in the dielectric is reduced by a factor of ϵ_r.

Problem 2-2

What steps must be taken to modify Problem 1-9 if the charged region is replaced by a solid dielectric sphere?

Problem 2-3

Prove that

$$\rho' = -\frac{(\epsilon_r - 1)}{\epsilon_r}\rho \tag{2-49}$$

2.4 Dielectric Interfaces

We wish now to see what conditions govern the behavior of the electric field at the boundary of two different dielectrics. Let us consider **D** first and let it have the values shown in Fig. 2–9 for each of the two different dielectrics. A Gaussian surface in the form of a very flat cylinder—a pillbox—encloses a section of the interface. If the cylinder is extremely flat, then the contributions to the flux integrals over the curved surface vanish. Gauss' theorem (A–11) can be written as

$$\oint \mathbf{D}\cdot d\mathbf{A} = q = \int \rho\, dV \tag{2–50}$$

Let us assume that the dielectrics are uncharged, so that $\rho = 0$. In some cases, however, it is still possible for a surface charge σ to exist at the interface and $\rho\, dV$ reduces to $\sigma\, dA$. We then have

$$\mathbf{D}_1 \cdot d\mathbf{A} - \mathbf{D}_2 \cdot d\mathbf{A} = \sigma\, dA \tag{2-51}$$

Each term on the left can be written in terms of its normal component as follows

$$\mathbf{D} \cdot d\mathbf{A} = D_n\, dA \tag{2-52}$$

so that (2–51) becomes

$$\mathbf{D}_{n1} - \mathbf{D}_{n2} = \sigma \tag{2-53}$$

In the particular case where there is no surface charge at the interface, Eq. (2–53) tells us that the normal component of **D** is continuous across the boundary.

We may place the pillbox at the interface between a conductor and a dielectric. Now we know that $\mathbf{D} = 0$ everywhere inside the conductor, including the walls of the pillbox; and, further, it must be normal to the interface just on the other side. Hence, we see that

$$\mathbf{D} \cdot d\mathbf{A} = \mathbf{D}_n dA = D\, dA = \sigma\, dA$$

or

$$\mathbf{D} = \sigma$$

where σ is the surface charge at the interface.

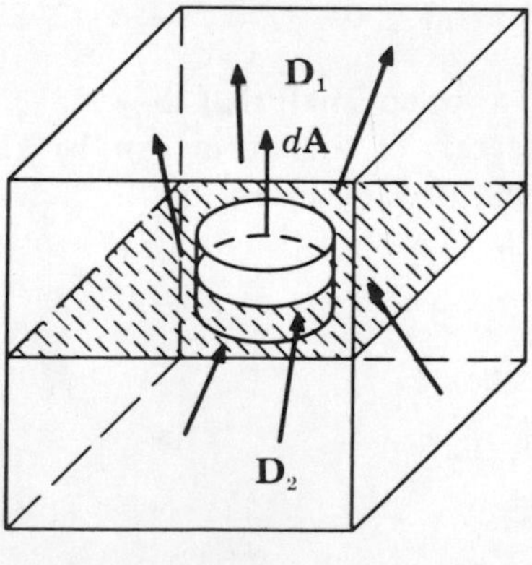

Fig. 2-9 A Gaussian surface at the interface between two dielectrics.

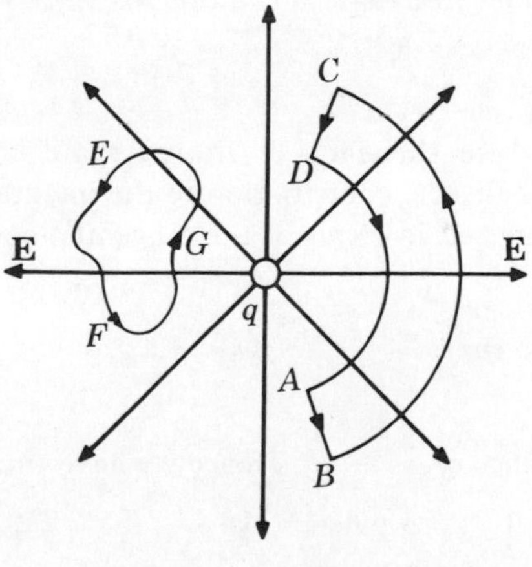

Fig. 2-10 Two equivalent closed paths in an electric field.

We can deduce a similar result for the tangential component of E, but first we must introduce the concept of a *conservative field.* Consider the radial field due to a point-charge q shown in Fig. 2–10. If we move a small positive charge around the path $ABCDA$, no work is done on sections BC or DA of the path, since the displacement is everywhere normal to $\mathbf{E}$. The amount of work done *on* the charge in moving it along CD equals the amount of work done *by* it in moving from A to B, and the total energy required to go around this closed path is zero. From the definition of work, which is

$$W = \int \mathbf{F} \cdot d\mathbf{l}$$

we can write

$$\oint \mathbf{E} \cdot d\mathbf{l} = 0 \tag{2-54}$$

where the symbol $\oint$ again denotes a closed path of integration. The left-hand side of this equation constitutes what is known as a *line integral*. The rigorous theory of such integrals is fairly involved, and we shall therefore treat them in a highly intuitive manner.

The result expressed by Eq. (2-54) also holds for a path EFG of arbitrary shape, since only the component of $\mathbf{E}$ in the radial direction contributes to the integral, and the work going along the direction of increasing radius is balanced by that in the other direction. This equation is essentially a statement of the principle of conservation of energy and accounts for the name given to the field.

If we now choose a closed path lying across the dielectric interface, as shown in Fig. (2-11), then by (2-54)

$$\oint \mathbf{E} \cdot d\mathbf{l} = \int \mathbf{E}_1 \cdot d\mathbf{l} - \int \mathbf{E}_2 \cdot d\mathbf{l} = 0 \tag{2-55}$$

where the ends of the path are chosen to be so small that they make a negligible contribution to the integral. Integrals of this form can be expressed in terms of the tangential component of $\mathbf{E}$ by using

$$\mathbf{E} \cdot d\mathbf{l} = E_t \, dl$$

so that

$$E_{t1} - E_{t2} = 0$$

since $dl_1 = -dl_2$. Hence we have the result that

$$E_{t1} = E_{t2} \tag{2-56}$$

showing that the tangential component of $\mathbf{E}$ is continuous across the boundary. This condition was derived using the assumption that the field $\mathbf{E}$ is conservative. However, we shall show later that Eq. (2-56) is valid under more general conditions.

Going back to (2-53) for $\sigma = 0$, we have

$$D_{n1} = D_{n2}$$

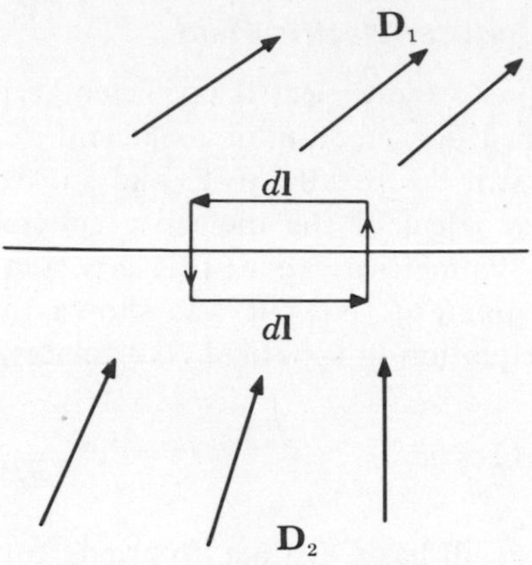

Fig. 2-11 A path enclosing a section of a dielectric interface.

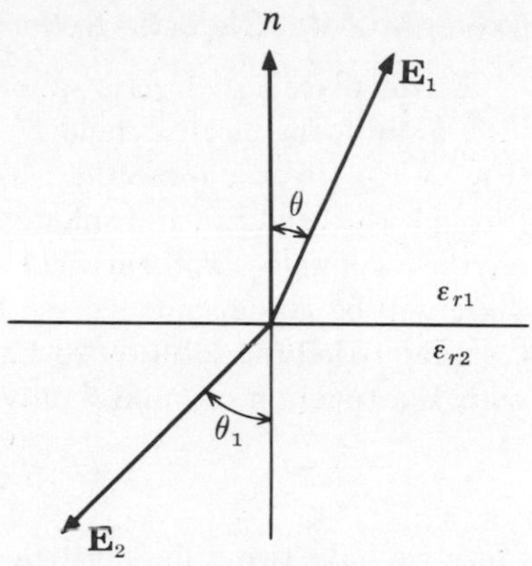

Fig. 2-12 Refraction of the lines of force at a dielectric interface.

or

$$\epsilon_{r1}\epsilon_v E_{n1} = \epsilon_{r2}\epsilon_v E_{n2} \tag{2-57}$$

Dividing this by Eq. (2–56) gives

$$\frac{\epsilon_{r1}}{\epsilon_{r2}} = \frac{\tan\theta_1}{\tan\theta_2} \tag{2-58}$$

where θ_1 is the angle which $\mathbf{E}_1$ makes to the normal at the interface (Fig. 2–12). This relation is somewhat like Snell's law in optics and indicates that there is a refraction of the lines of force at the interface. Further, if medium 1 is air and medium 2 is a dielectric, then $\epsilon_{r2} > \epsilon_{r1}$ and $\theta_2 > \theta_1$, as shown in Fig. 2–12.

Example 2-3 Capacitor with Dielectric Slab

A dielectric slab is inserted between the plates of the parallel-plate capacitor of Fig. 1–16. By (2–35), the field is

$$E = \frac{\sigma}{\epsilon_r \epsilon_v} \tag{2-59}$$

The difference in potential between the plates is then

$$V = Ed$$

and the capacitance is

$$C = \frac{\epsilon_r \epsilon_v A}{d} \tag{2-60}$$

which is a factor of ϵ_r greater than the capacity without the dielectric slab, as can be seen from Eq. (1–91).

Example 2-4 Dielectic Sphere in a Uniform Electric Field

Let us place a dielectric sphere of radius a and dielectric coefficient ϵ_{r1} into a uniform electric field $\mathbf{E}_0$ established in a medium of coefficient ϵ_{r2} (Fig. 2–13). If we choose the z-axis so that it lies parallel to $\mathbf{E}_0$ and passes through the center of the sphere, then any effect of the dielectric sphere on the originally uniform field will be symmetrical about this axis, and there will be no dependence on the coordinate ϕ. Now it was shown in Chapter 1 that the solution to Laplace's equation in spherical coordinates, with V a function of r and θ only, is

$$V = Ar\cos\theta + \frac{B\cos\theta}{r^2} \tag{1-57}$$

Since we have two different dielectrics, we will have distinct solutions for the region inside the sphere and for the exterior; we denote these by the subscripts I and E, respectively, so that we have

$$\left.\begin{aligned} V_I &= A_I r\cos\theta + B_I\frac{\cos\theta}{r^2} \\ V_E &= A_E r\cos\theta + B_E\frac{\cos\theta}{r^2} \end{aligned}\right\} \tag{2-61}$$

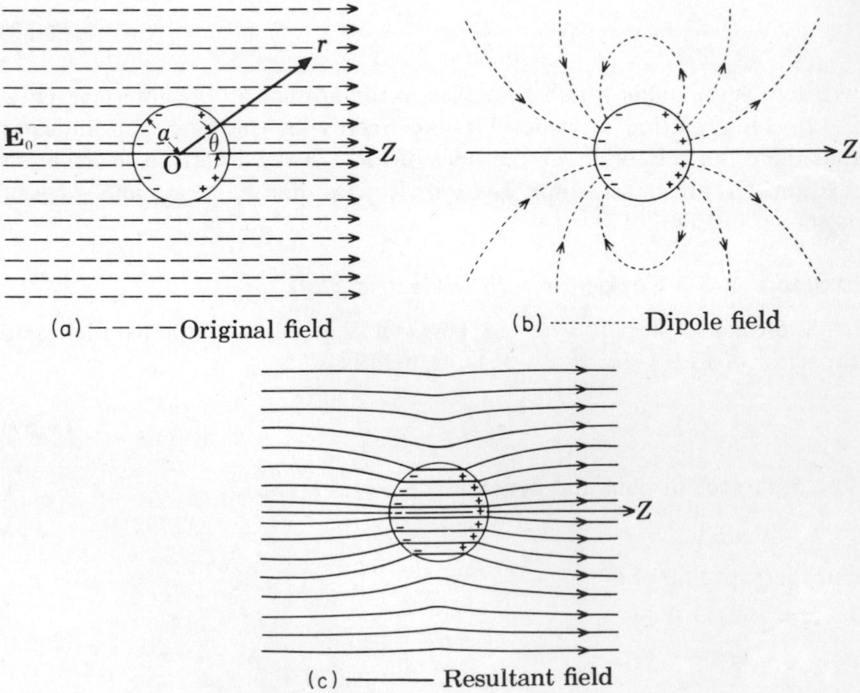

Fig. 2-13 A dielectric sphere in an originally uniform electric field.

One of the boundary conditions is that V_E must reduce to

$$V_E = -E_0 r \cos\theta = -E_0 z$$

as r becomes infinite, so that $A_E = -E_0$. Another is that V_I must remain finite at $r = 0$, making $B_I = 0$. The equations in (2–61) then become

$$V_I = A_I r \cos\theta$$
$$V_E = -E_0 r \cos\theta + \frac{B_E \cos\theta}{r^2} \tag{2–62}$$

and we now use the boundary conditions that E_t and D_n are continuous at at $r = a$, or from (1–36) we obtain

$$\frac{\partial V_E}{\partial\theta} = \frac{\partial V_I}{\partial\theta}, \qquad \epsilon_{r2}\frac{\partial V_E}{\partial r} = \epsilon_{r1}\frac{\partial V_I}{\partial r} \tag{2–63}$$

Combining these equations with (2–62) and solving for A_I and B_E, we obtain

$$A_I = \frac{-3\epsilon_{r2}E_0}{\epsilon_{r1} + 2\epsilon_{r2}}, \qquad B_E = \frac{(\epsilon_{r1} - \epsilon_{r2})a^3 E_0}{\epsilon_{r1} + 2\epsilon_{r2}} \tag{2–64}$$

For simplicity, let us now assume that the medium outside the sphere is a vacuum so that $\epsilon_{r2} = 1$. The potential inside the sphere can be written as

$$V_I = \frac{-3E_0 z}{\epsilon_r + 2} \tag{2–65}$$

where the subscript can be omitted from ϵ_{r1}, and the corresponding field is

$$E_I = -\frac{\partial V_I}{\partial z} = \frac{3E_0}{\epsilon_r + 2} \tag{2–66}$$

Since $\epsilon_r > 1$, the internal field is smaller than the original field $\mathbf{E}_0$ existing before the sphere was introduced. We note, however, that the new field $\mathbf{E}_I$ is still uniform and parallel to the z-axis. The reduction in $\mathbf{E}_0$ is due to the induced polarization, as we have already pointed out in connection with Example 2–2. That is, the field $\mathbf{E}_0$ induces a dipole moment per unit volume; the dipoles, in turn, set up a field which opposes the original field. The figure shows how the field $\mathbf{E}_0$ (dashed lines) and the dipole field (dotted lines) combine to give the resultant field (solid lines).

Problem 2–4

(a) Show analytically that the external potential is the sum of the potentials due to the original field and the polarized sphere.

(b) Why is the original external field changed by the presence of the sphere only in a region relatively close to the sphere?

2.5 The Depolarizing Factor

In considering both the point-charge in a dielectric (Example 2–2) and the dielectric sphere in a uniform field (Example 2–4), we have found that the dipoles induced in the material established a field which opposed the field originally applied to the material. This effect is known as *depolarization*, and the opposing dipole field is called the *depolarizing field* $\mathbf{E}_{\text{dep}}$. For the dielectric sphere, this quantity is the difference between the original field $\mathbf{E}_0$ and the internal field $\mathbf{E}_I$, or

$$\mathbf{E}_{\text{dep}} = \mathbf{E}_0 - \mathbf{E}_I = \mathbf{E}_0\left(1 - \frac{3}{\epsilon_r + 2}\right) = \frac{\epsilon_r - 1}{\epsilon_r + 2}\mathbf{E}_0 \tag{2–67}$$

We can then define a *depolarizing factor* L as the ratio

$$L = \frac{\epsilon_v E_{\text{dep}}}{P} \tag{2–68}$$

where $\mathbf{P}$ is the polarization and the use of ϵ_v makes L dimensionless. By combining (2–32) and (2–34), we obtain

$$\mathbf{P} = \epsilon_v(\epsilon_r - 1)\mathbf{E} \tag{2–69}$$

and the depolarizing factor for the sphere then becomes

$$L = \frac{\epsilon_v\left(\dfrac{\epsilon_r - 1}{\epsilon_r + 2}\right)E_0}{\epsilon_v(\epsilon_r - 1)\left(\dfrac{3E_0}{\epsilon_r + 2}\right)} = \frac{1}{3} \tag{2–70}$$

We note that this value of L holds only for a sphere.

The depolarization factor is defined in terms of the internal electric field. It is also interesting to study the behavior of $\mathbf{D}$ inside the dielectric sphere. From (2–66) and (2–35), we obtain

$$D_I = \frac{3\epsilon_r \epsilon_v E_0}{\epsilon_r + 2} \tag{2–71}$$

Since ϵ_r is greater than unity for a dielectric, this equation shows that D_I is greater than the applied electric displacement D_0, given by

$$D_0 = \epsilon_v E_0 \tag{2–72}$$

We thus find that the internal field is smaller than the applied field, whereas the opposite is true for $\mathbf{D}$. In fact, for large values of ϵ_r, (2–66) and (2–71) show that

$$\frac{E_I}{E_0} = \frac{3}{\epsilon_r}, \qquad \frac{D_I}{D_0} = 3 \tag{2–73}$$

We have indicated this by the change in thickness of the field lines in Fig. 2–14.

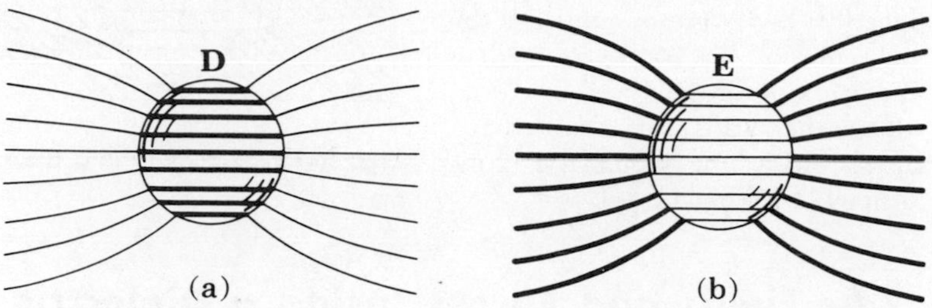

Fig. 2-14 The field and the displacement for a dielectric sphere.

Example 2-5 Depolarizing Factor for a Long, Thin Rod Parallel to E_0

A long, thin rod is placed in the field $\mathbf{E}_0$ with its axis parallel to $\mathbf{E}_0$. We use boundary condition

$$E_{t1} = E_{t2} \tag{2-56}$$

across the curved surface of the rod and ignore any contribution from the ends which are very small in area. Then we obtain

$$E_I = E_0 \tag{2-74}$$

This result shows that

$$\mathbf{E}_{\text{dep}} = \mathbf{E}_0 - \mathbf{E}_I = 0 \tag{2-75}$$

Therefore, there is no depolarizing effect inside the rod.

Problem 2-5

A thin, flat dielectric disc is placed in an electric field $\mathbf{E}_0$ with its round faces perpendicular to $\mathbf{E}_0$. Show that

(a) $\mathbf{E}_I = \mathbf{E}_0/\epsilon_r$ (2-76)

(b) $\mathbf{D}_I = \mathbf{D}_0$ (2-77)

(c) $L = 1$ (2-78)

Problem 2-6

A dielectric cylinder is placed in a field $\mathbf{E}_0$ with its axis perpendicular to $\mathbf{E}_0$. Show that

$$L = \frac{1}{2} \tag{2-79}$$

Problem 2-7

Figure 2-15 shows a block of dielectric in which has been established a uniform field **E**. If a spherical cavity is now cut out of the center of the block, show that the behavior of the lines of force along the walls of the cavity agrees with the boundary conditions (2-53) and (2-56).

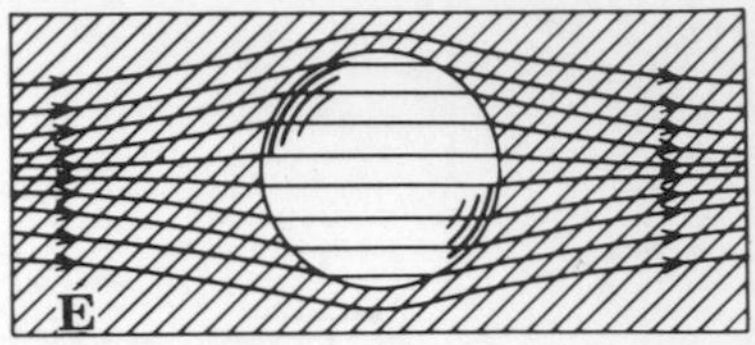

Fig. 2-15 A cavity in a dielectric medium.

2.6 Fields and Forces Inside a Dielectric

At this point, it is worthwhile to consider a theoretical concept of electrostatics which we have glossed over in the first part of this chapter. The idea to which we are referring is the notion of the field inside a dielectric. Let us recall that in Section 1.3 we defined the intensity **E** of a field in vacuum as the force per unit charge which a point-charge would "see" at each point in the field. If we now try to apply this definition in a dielectric, we are faced with several complications. First of all, in order to introduce a charge into the dielectric, we must make some kind of cavity, and this will change the value of the field at the point of measurement. Secondly, the introduction of a charge into a dielectric affects the value of the polarization **P**, which in turn also changes the value of **E**. We meet these complications by using the results of some previous calculations. It was shown in Problem 2-7 that a spherical cavity in a dielectric can be treated in the same way as a dielectric sphere in air. Applying this reasoning to the long, thin rod of Example 2-5 (and following a suggestion made by Lord Kelvin), we realize that a needle-shaped cavity can be drilled into a dielectric without changing the value of the internal field. However, the cavity must be very thin, so that we are faced with the experimental difficulty of actually making the force measurement. We realize that this provides us with a conceptual basis for defining **E** inside a dielectric, but that we cannot actually measure **E** in this fashion. An excellent discussion of this point will be found in the report of the Coulomb's Law Committee of the American Association of Physics Teachers [*Am. J. Phys.* **18**, 1 and 69, (1950)].

Another approach to the problem of defining the field in a dielectric is possible if we are working with liquids. Assuming that the material is a Class A dielectric, we can establish a field in it by immersing a charge q_1 and then measure the force on a second charge q_2 with some kind of strain gauge. The field on q_2, from Example 2-2, is

$$\mathbf{E} = \frac{q_1}{4\pi\epsilon_r\epsilon_v r^2}\mathbf{r}_0 \tag{2–41}$$

and the force on q_2 is then

$$\mathbf{F} = q_2\mathbf{E} = \frac{q_1 q_2 \mathbf{r}_0}{4\pi\epsilon_r\epsilon_v r^2} \tag{2–80}$$

This relation has the same form as Coulomb's law (1–6), with the inclusion of a factor ϵ_r in the denominator. However, it is deceptively simple in appearance, since the force **F** involves not only the direct attraction between the two charges but also the interactions between each charge and the induced dipoles in the medium, and all of these forces are automatically taken care of by the factor $1/\epsilon_r$.

2.7 Energy Density in Dielectrics

The development of Section 1.10 can be extended to dielectrics without difficulty. Equation (1–130) expresses the energy of a charge distribution as

$$W = \frac{1}{2}\int \rho V \, d\bar{V} \tag{2–81}$$

and we can carry this over directly. Restricting what follows to free charges, we can use

$$\operatorname{div} \mathbf{D} = \rho \tag{2–31}$$

Then by the vector identity (A–3), we obtain

$$W = \frac{1}{2}\int \operatorname{div}(V\mathbf{D})\, d\bar{V} - \frac{1}{2}\int \mathbf{D}\cdot\mathbf{grad}\, V\, d\bar{V} \tag{2–82}$$

We next convert the first term to a surface integral as we did to obtain (1–132), and then show that it falls off as $1/r$ for a large surface, leaving

$$W = \frac{1}{2}\int \mathbf{D}\cdot\mathbf{E}\, d\bar{V} \tag{2–83}$$

We also introduce the energy density E_V, getting, in analogy with (1–133), the equation

$$E_V = \frac{1}{2}\mathbf{D}\cdot\mathbf{E} \tag{2–84}$$

For the special case of a Class A dielectric

$$\mathbf{D} = \epsilon_r\epsilon_v\mathbf{E} \tag{2–35}$$

and (2–83) becomes

$$W = \frac{\epsilon_r\epsilon_v}{2}\int E^2\, d\bar{V} \tag{2–85}$$

3 Electromagnetic Fields in Free Space

3.1 Electric Current and Current Density

Moving charges are said to constitute an *electric current*. Quantitatively, we define current I by

$$I = \frac{dq}{dt} \tag{3-1}$$

so that the MKS unit of current, known as the *ampere*, is equivalent to a coulomb/second. It is also convenient to define *current density* $\mathbf{J}$ as the electric current per unit area passing across a surface which is perpendicular to the direction of flow. For the conducting, rectangular block of Fig. 3–1, the current and current density are related by

$$|\mathbf{J}| = \frac{I}{A} \tag{3-2}$$

and **J** has units of amperes/meter². If the current is produced by a difference of potential V between the ends of the block, the ratio V/I is called the *resistance* R of the metal, and the MKS unit of resistance is the *ohm*. Thus

$$V = IR \tag{3-3}$$

and this relation is one form of *Ohm's law*. The resistance of a unit cube of a material is called the *resistivity* or *specific resistance* ρ, and the reciprocal of ρ is known as the conductivity σ, or

$$\sigma = \frac{1}{\rho} \tag{3-4}$$

It is found experimentally that the resistance of a block of metal is directly proportional to the length l and inversely proportional to the area A, so that

$$R = \frac{\rho l}{A} \tag{3-5}$$

where ρ serves as the proportionality constant. From (3-3) we see that

$$V = \frac{I(\rho l)}{A} = Jl\rho \tag{3-6}$$

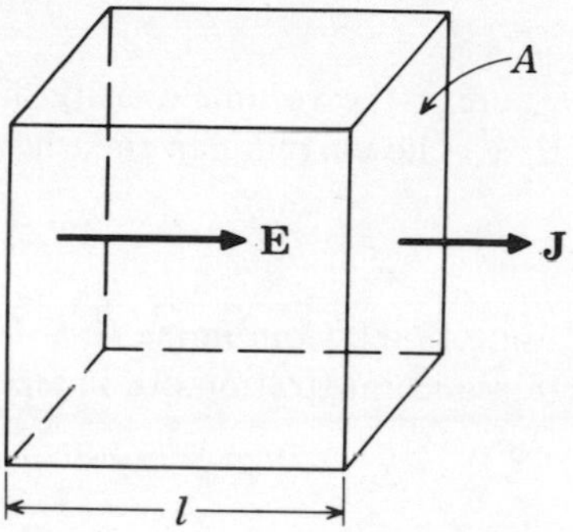

Fig. 3-1 **Relation between field, current, and current-density in a conductor.**

and using the relation

$$V = -\int \mathbf{E} \cdot d\mathbf{l} \tag{3-7}$$

we obtain

$$V = -\int_l^0 Edx = El \tag{3-8}$$

so that 3-6 becomes

$$E = \rho J \tag{3-9}$$

or by (3-4),

$$J = \sigma E \tag{3-10}$$

Since **J** and **E** are colinear in the figure, we can write (3-10) in vector form as

$$\mathbf{J} = \sigma \mathbf{E} \tag{3-11}$$

If we now consider a current density **J** flowing across a surface dA at an arbitrary angle, the corresponding current is

$$I = \int \mathbf{J} \cdot d\mathbf{A} \tag{3-12}$$

and for a closed surface S

$$I = \oint \mathbf{J} \cdot d\mathbf{A} \tag{3–13}$$

By the divergence theorem (A–11), this becomes

$$I = \int \operatorname{div} \mathbf{J} \, dV \tag{3–14}$$

The total charge present in this volume at any given time is

$$q = \int \rho(x, y, z, t) \, dV \tag{3–15}$$

where ρ, the volume density of charge, depends on both position $\mathbf{r}$ and on time. The current can then be expressed

$$I = \frac{\partial q}{\partial t} \tag{3–16}$$

using (3–1). Combining this with (3–15) and assuming that the differentiation and integration are independent operations, we have

$$I = \int \frac{\partial \rho}{\partial t} \, dV \tag{3–17}$$

Now the current given by (3–13) or (3–14) represents the net flow across the outside of the bounding surface whereas the current of (3–17) is the current due to the loss of charge on the inside, and, hence, it is a negative quantity with respect to the exterior current. Equating the two currents, then, gives

$$\int \left(\operatorname{div} \mathbf{J} + \frac{\partial \rho}{\partial t} \right) dV = 0$$

or

$$\operatorname{div} \mathbf{J} + \frac{\partial \rho}{\partial t} = 0 \tag{3–18}$$

This is called the *equation of continuity* and is a mathematical expression of the principle of conservation of charge. By using Ohm's law (3–11), the Maxwell equation (2–31), and the relation (2–35),

$$\operatorname{div} \mathbf{D} = \bar{\rho}, \qquad \mathbf{D} = \epsilon_r \epsilon_v \mathbf{E} \tag{3–19}$$

where the bar on the symbol $\bar{\rho}$ for volume-charge density is to distinguish it from resistivity ρ, we obtain

$$\operatorname{div} \mathbf{J} = \operatorname{div} (\sigma \mathbf{E}) = \operatorname{div} \left(\frac{\sigma \mathbf{D}}{\epsilon_r \epsilon_v} \right) = \frac{\overline{\sigma \rho}}{\epsilon_r \epsilon_v} \tag{3–20}$$

so that (3–18) becomes

$$\frac{\partial \bar{\rho}}{\partial t} + \left(\frac{\sigma}{\epsilon_r \epsilon_v} \right) \bar{\rho} = 0 \tag{3–21}$$

Problem 3-1

(a) Show that the quantity $(\sigma/\epsilon_r\epsilon_v)^{-1}$ has dimensions of time. It is called the *relaxation time* τ.

(b) Substitute τ into the differential equation (3-21) and solve it by the method of the separation of variables, using the boundary condition

$$\bar{\rho} = \bar{\rho}_0 \quad \text{at} \quad t = 0$$

(c) Calculate τ for copper, making a reasonable assumption for the value of ϵ_r.

(d) Give a physical interpretation of this solution.

(e) Two electrodes are immersed in a medium of conductivity σ and are connected to a circuit carrying a constant current I. By applying Gauss' law to one electrode (neglecting any error due to a small wire lead), show that the resistance R between the electrodes is related to their capacitance C_0 in free space by

$$RC_0 = \frac{\epsilon_v}{\sigma}$$

What is the relation between RC_0 and τ?

(f) A metal sphere is given a uniform volume charge $\bar{\rho}$, which immediately migrates to the surface. Express the surface charge σ as a function of time.

3.2 Current and Magnetism

If two neighboring wires are carrying currents I_1 and I_2, as shown in Fig. 3-2, we know experimentally that there will be a mutual attractive

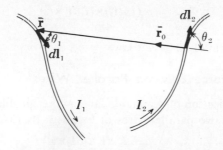

Fig. 3-2 The variables involved in Ampere's law.

or repulsive force, called the *magnetic force*. This force also depends on the spacing and relative orientation of the two wires. It can be shown experimentally (although indirectly) that the force $d\mathbf{F}_1$ on an element $d\mathbf{l}_1$ interacting with another element $d\mathbf{l}_2$ is proportional to all the variables shown in the figure, and this dependence can be expressed in the form

$$dF_1 \propto \begin{cases} dl_1 \\ dl_2 \\ I_1 \\ I_2 \\ \sin\theta_1 \\ \sin\theta_2 \\ \dfrac{1}{\bar{r}^2} \end{cases} \tag{3-22}$$

Further, there exists a definite geometical relation between $d\mathbf{l}_1$, $d\mathbf{l}_2$, $\bar{\mathbf{r}}$, and $d\mathbf{F}_1$, which can be expressed in terms of the vector product as

$$d\mathbf{F}_1 \propto \frac{(I_1 dl_1)\times[(I_2 dl_2)\times\bar{\mathbf{r}}_0]}{\bar{r}^2} \tag{3-23}$$

where $\bar{\mathbf{r}}_0$ is a unit vector along $\bar{\mathbf{r}}$ and where the sense of the vector products is based on experimental observation. To convert this into an equation, we choose a proportionality constant of the form $\mu_v/4\pi$ where μ_v is called the *permeability of free space* and to which we assign a value given exactly by

$$\mu_v = 4\pi \times 10^{-7} \text{ newton/ampere} \tag{3-24}$$

Problem 3-2

Verify the units used to express μ_v.

The precise value assigned to μ_v may seem strange at first glance, and we shall defer the explanation of this point until we consider wave motion. The relation (3-23) then becomes

$$d\mathbf{F}_1 = \frac{\mu_v(I_1 d\mathbf{l}_1)\times(I_2 d\mathbf{l}_2\times\bar{r}_0)}{4\pi\bar{r}^2} \tag{3-25}$$

and this is one form of *Ampere's law.*

Example 3-1 Force Between Parallel Wires

A simple application of Ampere's law is the problem of finding the force between the two parallel wires of Fig. 3-3. By (3-25)

$$d\mathbf{F}_1 = \frac{\mu_v I_1 I_2}{4\pi}\frac{d\mathbf{l}_1\times(d\mathbf{l}_2\times\bar{\mathbf{r}}_0)}{\bar{\mathbf{r}}^2} \tag{3-26}$$

The term in parentheses is a vector whose magnitude can be expressed by

$$\frac{dl_2}{\bar{r}^2}\sin\phi = \frac{dl_2}{\bar{r}^2}\cos\theta$$

This vector is normal to the plane of the paper and points toward the reader. Since

$$l_2 = a\tan\theta, \qquad \text{and} \qquad dl_2 = a\sec^2\theta\, d\theta$$

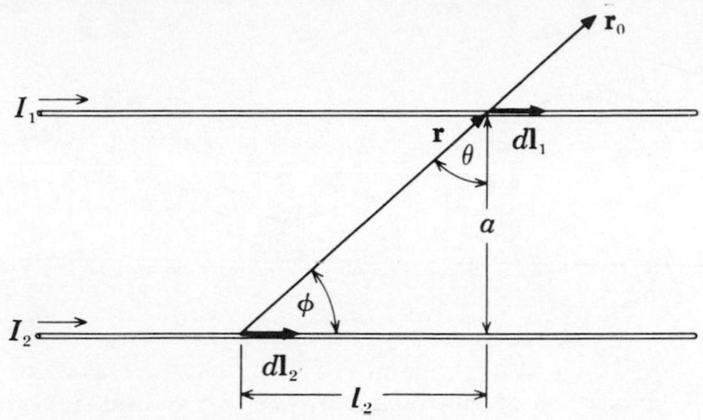

Fig. 3-3 Calculation of the force between two wires carrying currents.

then

$$\frac{dl_2 \cos\theta}{\bar{r}^2} = \frac{a \sec\theta \, d\theta}{a^2 \sec^2\theta}$$

Integrating over θ,

$$\int_{-\pi/2}^{\pi/2} \frac{\cos\theta \, d\theta}{a} = \frac{2}{a}$$

Since the vector $d\mathbf{l}_2 \times \bar{\mathbf{r}}_0$ is perpendicular to the plane of the two wires, it is perpendicular to $d\mathbf{l}_1$, and the force has a magnitude

$$dF_1 = \frac{\mu_v I_1 I_2}{2\pi a} \, dl_2$$

so that the force per unit length is

$$F_l = \frac{\mu_v I_1 I_2}{2\pi a} \tag{3-27}$$

The sense of the vector product makes $\mathbf{F}_l$ point towards the other wire; that is, when the currents flow in the same direction, then the force is attractive (and vice versa).

Returning now to (3–25), let us apply this equation to current-carrying circuits of arbitrary shape. If both conductors form closed loops (Fig. 3–4), then the force can be expressed as

$$\mathbf{F}_1 = \frac{\mu_v I_1 I_2}{4\pi} \oint\oint \frac{d\mathbf{l}_1 \times (d\mathbf{l}_2 \times \bar{\mathbf{r}}_0)}{\bar{r}^2} \tag{3-28}$$

The integrand can be rewritten using the vector identity

$$\mathbf{A} \times (\mathbf{B} \times \mathbf{C}) = \mathbf{B}(\mathbf{A} \cdot \mathbf{C}) - \mathbf{C}(\mathbf{A} \cdot \mathbf{B}) \tag{A-1}$$

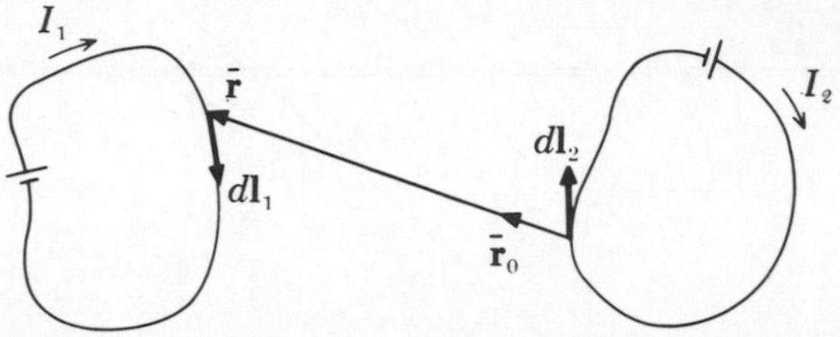

Fig. 3-4 Evaluation of the force between two current-carrying loops.

to obtain

$$d\mathbf{l}_1 \times (d\mathbf{l}_2 \times \bar{\mathbf{r}}_0) = d\mathbf{l}_2(d\mathbf{l}_1 \cdot \bar{\mathbf{r}}_0) - \bar{\mathbf{r}}_0(d\mathbf{l}_1 \cdot d\mathbf{l}_2) \tag{3-29}$$

and the integral involving the first term on the right is

$$\oint\oint \frac{d\mathbf{l}_2(d\mathbf{l}_1 \cdot \bar{\mathbf{r}}_0)}{\bar{r}^2} = -\oint\oint d\mathbf{l}_2 d\mathbf{l}_1 \cdot \mathbf{grad}\, \frac{1}{\bar{r}} \tag{3-30}$$

where we have used (2–20). By Stokes' theorem (A–14) and the identity (A–9), this integral can be further transformed, obtaining

$$\oint\oint d\mathbf{l}_2 d\mathbf{l}_1 \cdot \mathbf{grad}\, \frac{1}{\bar{r}} = \oint d\mathbf{l}_2 \int \mathbf{curl\ grad}\, \frac{1}{\bar{r}} \cdot d\mathbf{A} = 0 \tag{3-31}$$

Hence, (3–28) becomes

$$\mathbf{F}_1 = \frac{\mu_0 I_1 I_2}{4\pi} \oint\oint \frac{\bar{\mathbf{r}}_0}{\bar{r}^2}\, d\mathbf{l}_1 \cdot d\mathbf{l}_2 \tag{3-32}$$

which is symmetric with respect to the two loops. Calculating the force on the other loop in the same manner, we obtain

$$\mathbf{F}_2 = -\mathbf{F}_1$$

as would be expected.

3.3 Magnetic Induction

Equation (3–28) can be used to obtain a qualitative description of the magnetic field by writing it as

$$\mathbf{F}_1 = I_1 \int d\mathbf{l}_1 \times \mathbf{B}_2 \tag{3-33}$$

where $\mathbf{B}_2$ is called the *magnetic induction*, or *magnetic flux density*, and is given by

$$\mathbf{B}_2 = \frac{\mu_0 I_2}{4\pi} \oint \frac{d\mathbf{l}_2 \times \bar{\mathbf{r}}_0}{\bar{r}^2} \tag{3-34}$$

Equation (3–34), which we will use as the definition of **B**, is known as the *Biot-Savart* law. We can interpret it as meaning that the force on loop 1 depends on (a) its own current; (b) its geometrical relation to loop 2; and (c) the strength of the magnetic field produced by loop 2, as determined by **B**. The unit of magnetic induction is the *weber/meter²*. Another unit which is still in common use is the *gauss*, where

$$10^4 \text{ gauss} = 1 \text{ weber/meter}^2$$

Problem 3-3

(a) Show that the product $\mu_v \epsilon_v$ has dimensions of $(\text{velocity})^{-2}$.

(b) Show that a weber is equivalent to a volt-second.

Problem 3-4

The electrons in a beam are all moving with constant velocity **v** at right angles to a uniform magnetic field **B**. Show that the force on the beam is given by

$$= -e(\mathbf{v} \times \mathbf{B}) \tag{3-35}$$

where e (1.6×10^{-19} coulomb) is the magnitude of the charge on the electron. Draw a sketch showing the sense and direction of the vectors **v**, **B**, and **F**.

Example 3-2 Induction Due to a Long, Straight Wire

The results of the previous example can be used to find the induction **B** due to a long, straight wire carrying a current I. Referring to Fig. 3–5, it was shown in Example 3–1 that

$$\int \frac{d\mathbf{l}_2 \times \bar{\mathbf{r}}_0}{\bar{r}^2} = \int_{-\pi/2}^{\pi/2} \frac{\cos\theta\, d\theta}{a} = \frac{2}{a}$$

so that

$$B = \frac{\mu_v I}{2\pi a} \tag{3-36}$$

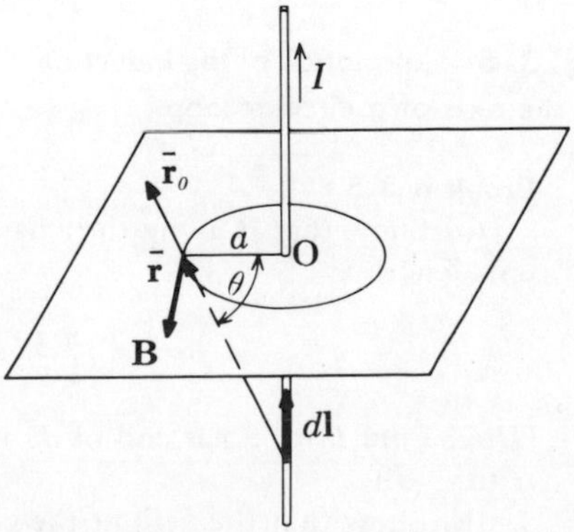

Fig. 3-5 Calculation of the induction due to a straight wire.

Equation (3–34) shows that $d\mathbf{l}$, $\bar{\mathbf{r}}_0$, and $\mathbf{B}$ form a right-handed system, and Eq. (3–36) indicates that the lines of $\mathbf{B}$ are circles in a plane perpendicular to the wire.

Example 3-3 Induction on Axis of Circular Coil

Consider a loop of radius a carrying a current I (Fig. 3–6). By symmetry, the resultant induction $d\mathbf{B}$ is along the z-axis, giving

$$dB_z = \frac{\mu_v I \, dl}{4\pi \, \bar{r}^2} \cos \alpha$$

But

$$\cos \alpha = \cos \phi = \frac{a}{\bar{r}}$$

Hence

$$B_z = \frac{\mu_v I a}{4\pi \bar{r}^3} \int_0^{2\pi a} dl = \frac{\mu_v I a^2}{2(a^2 + d^2)^{3/2}} \tag{3–37}$$

and in the plane of the coil

$$B_0 = \frac{\mu_v I}{2a} \tag{3–38}$$

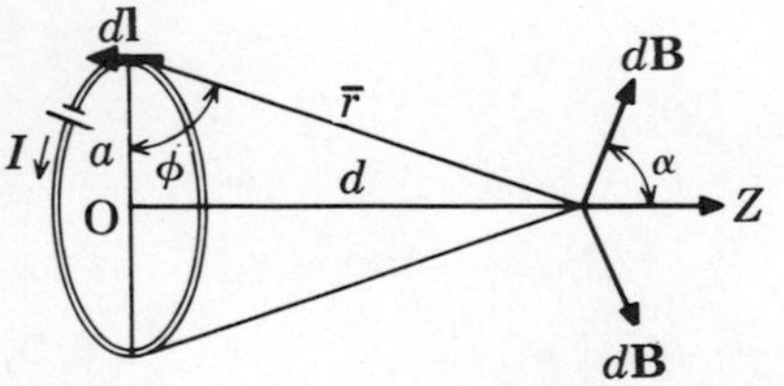

Fig. 3-6 Calculation of the induction on the axis of a circular loop.

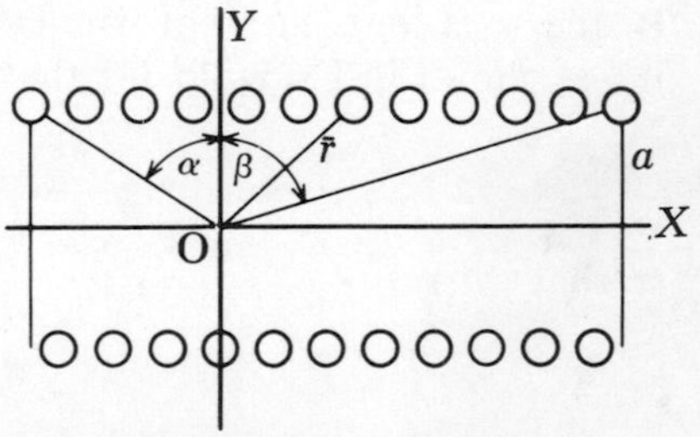

Fig. 3-7 A solenoid.

Problem 3-5

(a) Show that $\mathbf{B}$ along the axis of a solenoid (Fig. 3–7) with n_l turns per unit length is

$$B_x = \frac{\mu_v n_l I}{2} (\sin \alpha + \sin \beta)$$

(*Hint:* Find B for a flat coil of dn turns from Eq. (3–37) and integrate from α to $-\beta$.)

(b) Show that the field at the center of a long solenoid is given by the expression

$$B_x = \mu_v I n_l \tag{3-39}$$

(c) Show that the field at the ends is given

$$B_x = \frac{\mu_v I n_l}{2} \tag{3-40}$$

Problem 3-6

(a) When a particle moves in a curved path, it takes a force directed towards the center of curvature—the *centripetal force*—to keep it in this path. Show that for motion in a circle of radius R, the velocity is given by

$$v = R\frac{d\theta}{dt}$$

and the centripetal acceleration by

$$a_r = \frac{d^2x}{dt^2}\cos\theta + \frac{d^2y}{dt^2}\sin\theta = \frac{-v^2}{R} \tag{3-41}$$

where θ is the polar angular coordinate.

(b) Consider an electron moving with velocity $\mathbf{v}$ at right angles to a uniform magnetic field B. By using (3-35), show that the path is circular, with a radius R given by

$$R = \frac{mv}{eB}$$

(c) Show that the electron moves around this circle with an angular velocity

$$\omega = \frac{eB}{m} \tag{3-42}$$

called the *cyclotron frequency*.

3.4 Magnetic Vector Potential

The definition

$$\mathbf{B} = \frac{\mu_v I}{4\pi}\oint\frac{d\mathbf{l}\times\bar{\mathbf{r}}_0}{\bar{r}^2} \tag{3-34}$$

expresses the magnetic induction $\mathbf{B}$ at a point $\bar{\mathbf{r}}$ with respect to a current element $Id\mathbf{l}$ in a closed circuit (Fig. 3-8). Using the vector identity (2-20) Eq. (3-34) becomes

$$\mathbf{B} = \frac{\mu_v I}{4\pi}\oint \mathbf{grad}'\left(\frac{1}{\bar{r}}\right)\times d\mathbf{l} \tag{3-43}$$

where we have eliminated the negative sign by reversing the terms in the vector product. Using the identity (A-4) shows that the integrand can be

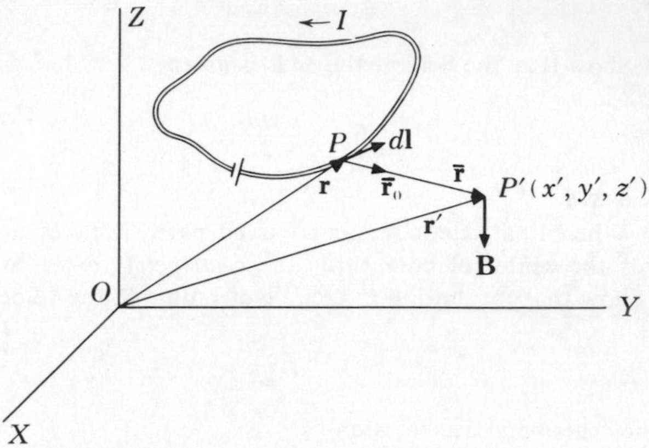

Fig. 3-8 The magnetic induction of a closed loop.

expressed by

$$\mathbf{grad}'\left(\frac{1}{\bar{r}}\right) \times d\mathbf{l} = \mathbf{curl}'\left(\frac{d\mathbf{l}}{\bar{r}}\right) - \frac{1}{\bar{r}}\,\mathbf{curl}'\,d\mathbf{l} \qquad (3\text{–}44)$$

where the prime still denotes differentiation with respect to (x', y', z'). The second term, however, vanishes, since $d\mathbf{l}$, located at point $P(x, y, z)$, is independent of the coordinates (x', y', z'). This leaves

$$\mathbf{B} = \frac{\mu_v I}{4\pi}\oint \mathbf{curl}'\left(\frac{d\mathbf{l}}{\bar{r}}\right) \qquad (3\text{–}45)$$

and since the differentiation and integration are with respect to two different sets of variables, (3–45) may be written

$$\mathbf{B} = \mathbf{curl}'\left[\frac{\mu_v I}{4\pi}\oint \frac{d\mathbf{l}}{\bar{r}}\right] \qquad (3\text{–}46)$$

We now define the *magnetic vector potential* **A** by

$$\mathbf{A}(x', y', z') = \frac{\mu_v I}{4\pi}\oint \frac{d\mathbf{l}}{\bar{r}} \qquad (3\text{–}47)$$

Problem 3-7

Show that magnetic vector potential has units of webers/meter.

Equation (3–46) may now be written as

$$\mathbf{B} = \mathbf{curl}'\,\mathbf{A} \qquad (3\text{–}48)$$

For simplicity, however, we shall write this relation between **A** and **B** as

$$\mathbf{B} = \mathbf{curl}\,\mathbf{A} \qquad (3\text{–}49)$$

bearing in mind that the differentiation must be performed with respect to the field coordinates.

Now using vector identity (A–8), we see that

$$\text{div}\,\mathbf{curl}\,\mathbf{A} = \text{div}\,\mathbf{B} = 0 \tag{3–50}$$

This is the *second Maxwell equation*, and it can be combined with the divergence theorem (A–11) to obtain

$$\int \text{div}\,\mathbf{B}\,dV = \oint \mathbf{B}\cdot d\bar{\mathbf{A}} = 0 \tag{3–51}$$

where we use the symbol $\bar{\mathbf{A}}$ for area whenever there is any danger of confusing it with the vector potential **A**. Recalling the physical interpretation of the divergence given in Sec. 1.8, Eq. (3–51) indicates that lines of magnetic induction are completely closed; that is, they do not terminate on magnetic poles in the same way that electric lines of force terminate on free charges. Hence, Maxwell's second law is a mathematical statement of the experimental fact that isolated magnetic poles do not exist.

By Stokes' theorem (A–14), we also have

$$\int \mathbf{B}\cdot d\bar{\mathbf{A}} = \int \mathbf{curl}\,\mathbf{A}\cdot d\bar{\mathbf{A}} = \oint \mathbf{A}\cdot d\mathbf{l} \tag{3–52}$$

The integral involving **B** is the flux of **B** over the surface $\bar{A}$, in accordance with definition (1–16). This quantity is so useful that we shall denote it by its own symbol Φ and refer to it as the *magnetic flux*, so that

$$\Phi = \int \mathbf{B}\cdot d\bar{\mathbf{A}} \tag{3–53}$$

We can then see from (3–53) why **B** is called the *magnetic flux density*, since it has dimensions of flux per unit area.

Problem 3-8

A cube of edge $2d$ has its center at the origin of the axes $OXYZ$ and its faces parallel to the coordinate planes. A straight wire located along the z-axis carries a current I in the positive direction. Find the flux across the face $x = d$.

3.5 Electromagnetic Induction

It was discovered independently by Faraday and Henry that a varying magnetic field can produce an electric current in a closed circuit, and this process is known as *electromagnetic induction*. Further, it has been found that the induced current will establish a magnetic field which opposes the original varying field, and this phenomenon is called *Lenz's law;* it is a consequence of the principle of conservation of energy as applied to electromagnetic effects.

Now consider an element $d\mathbf{l}$ of conductor moving in a uniform magnetic field $\mathbf{B}$ (Fig. 3–9). If we connect this element to a meter with flexible leads, then a current I and a difference of potential V will be induced in the closed circuit. Let the element $d\mathbf{l}$ undergo a displacement $d\mathbf{r}$ parallel to itself, and requiring a time dt. The magnitude of the work done is

$$dW = \mathbf{F}\cdot d\mathbf{r}$$

By (3–33) this becomes

$$dW = Id\mathbf{l} \times \mathbf{B}\cdot d\mathbf{r} = Id\mathbf{r} \times d\mathbf{l}\cdot\mathbf{B}$$
$$= I\mathbf{B}\cdot d\mathbf{A} \qquad (3\text{–}54)$$

since the area swept out is

$$d\mathbf{A} = d\mathbf{r} \times d\mathbf{l}$$

Now the flux over the area dS is, by (3–53),

$$d\Phi = \mathbf{B}\cdot d\mathbf{A}$$

so that

$$dW = Id\Phi \qquad (3\text{–}55)$$

The amount of charge set in motion by the induction process is

$$dq = Idt$$

so that

$$dW = Vdq = VIdt$$

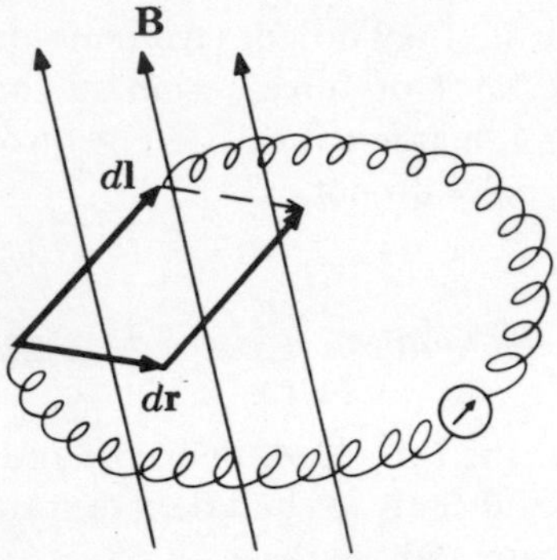

Fig. 3-9 Derivation of Faraday's law.

Equating this to (3–55) gives

$$V = \frac{d\Phi}{dt} \qquad (3\text{–}56)$$

which is *Faraday's law*. This can be put in another form by using (1–34), giving

$$\oint \mathbf{E}\cdot d\mathbf{l} = -\frac{d\Phi}{dt} \qquad (3\text{–}57)$$

The line-integral on the left-hand side of this equation is called the *electromotance*. An older name is *electromotive force* or *emf*, but this is not a satisfactory term, since the dimensions are those of work per unit charge —that is, potential. Hence, for simplicity, we shall also refer to this quantity as *voltage*.

Example 3-4 Expanding Rectangular Loop

The rectangular loop of Fig. 3–10 has a traveling side moving to the right with a velocity $\mathbf{v}$. The loop is placed in a uniform magnetic field $\mathbf{B}$, which is normal to its plane. The potential difference produced at the meter is

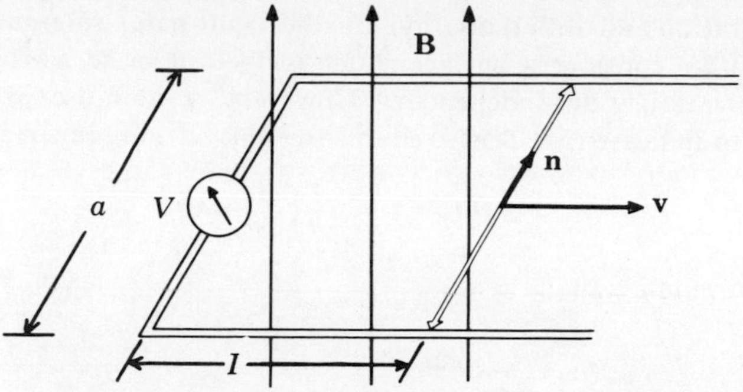

Fig. 3-10 Induced potential in a sliding wire.

obtained by computing $d\Phi/dt$. Now

$$d\Phi = \mathbf{B}\cdot d\mathbf{A}$$

and
$$\frac{d\Phi}{dt} = \mathbf{B}\cdot\frac{d\mathbf{A}}{dt} \tag{3-58}$$

since **B** is a constant. But

$$\frac{dA}{dt} = a\frac{dl}{dt} = av$$

Hence,
$$V = Bav$$

This result may also be obtained from (3–57), when combined with (3–35). For

$$\mathbf{E} = \frac{\mathbf{F}}{e} = -\mathbf{v}\times\mathbf{B}$$

and

$$\oint \mathbf{E}\cdot d\mathbf{l} = -\oint \mathbf{v}\times\mathbf{B}\cdot d\mathbf{l}$$

We notice that

$$\mathbf{v}\times\mathbf{B} = vB\mathbf{n}$$

where **n** is a unit vector oriented as shown. Integrating over the moving arm,

$$V = -Bv\int_0^a \mathbf{n}\cdot d\mathbf{l} = Bav \tag{3-59}$$

as above.

The results above can be put in another form by applying Stokes' theorem to Faraday's law. Then, (3–57) becomes

$$\int \textbf{curl } \mathbf{E}\cdot d\mathbf{A} = \frac{-d}{dt}\int \mathbf{B}\cdot d\mathbf{A} \tag{3-60}$$

The integration and differentiation on the right-hand side can be interchanged if we consider a surface which is fixed in space, so that the time and space variables are independent. However, we now use partial differentiation to indicate that **B** is fixed in space but varying in time, obtaining

$$\int \textbf{curl } \mathbf{E} \cdot d\mathbf{A} = -\int \frac{\partial \mathbf{B}}{\partial t} \cdot d\mathbf{A} \qquad \textbf{(3–61)}$$

and equating integrands

$$\textbf{curl } \mathbf{E} = \frac{-\,\partial \mathbf{B}}{\partial t} \qquad \textbf{(3–62)}$$

This is the *third Maxwell equation*, and it is essentially a statement of Faraday's law.

Problem 3-9

A stiff wire is bent into a semi-circle of radius R and rotated with a frequency f in a uniform field **B**, as shown in Fig. 3–11. Find the amplitude and frequency of the generated voltage.

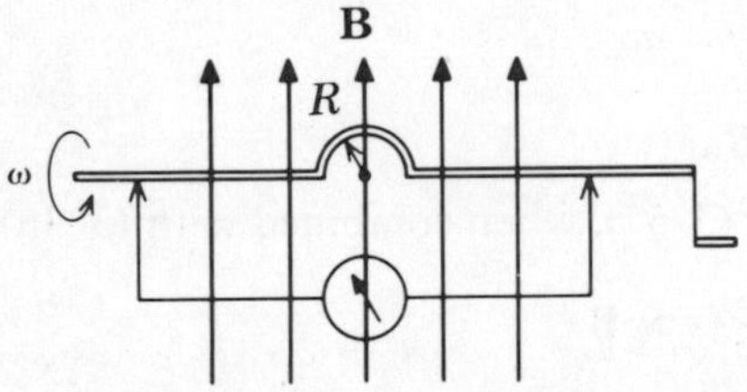

Fig. 3-11 An application of Faraday's law. (From A. F. Kip, op. cit., with permission.)

3.6 Inductance

Suppose we have a coil of wire carrying an alternating current. This current produces a varying field **B** which in turn induces a current in the coil; and the induced current, by Lenz's law, opposes the original current. The rate of change of enclosed flux with current is called the coefficient of *self-induction* or *inductance L*, so that

$$L = \frac{d\Phi}{dI} \qquad \textbf{(3–63)}$$

and the MKS unit is the *henry*. The induced voltage is then

$$V = \frac{d\Phi}{dt} = L\frac{dI}{dt} \qquad \textbf{(3–64)}$$

Problem 3–10

Prove that the henry is the proper unit for inductance.

Example 3-5 Inductance of a Solenoid

Consider a long solenoid of n turns, such as the one of Fig. 3–7. Using (3–39) and the fact that $\sin\alpha$ and $\sin\beta$ will be approximately equal to unity, we obtain

$$B_x = \mu_v nI/l \tag{3-65}$$

for the induction, where l is the length. The corresponding flux is

$$\Phi = BA = \mu_v nIA/l \tag{3-66}$$

where A is the cross-sectional area. Hence, the induced voltage for one turn is

$$V_1 = \frac{d\Phi}{dt} = \frac{\mu_v nA}{l}\frac{dI}{dt} \tag{3-67}$$

and for the entire n turns

$$V = \frac{\mu_v n^2 A}{l}\frac{dI}{dt} \tag{3-68}$$

Then

$$L = \mu_v n^2 A/l \tag{3-69}$$

If two coils are arranged so that the changing flux due to one of them causes a current to be induced in the other, they are said to form a *mutual inductance* or *transformer*. The quantitative definition of the *coefficient of mutual inductance* L_{12} is

$$L_{12} = \frac{d\Phi_2}{dI_1} \tag{3-70}$$

Example 3-6 Mutual Inductance with Perfect Coupling

Consider two coils of the same length and cross section, but with n_1 and n_2 turns, respectively, arranged so that the flux due to either one is common to both (Fig. 3–12). The voltage in coil 2 due to coil 1, by (3–67),

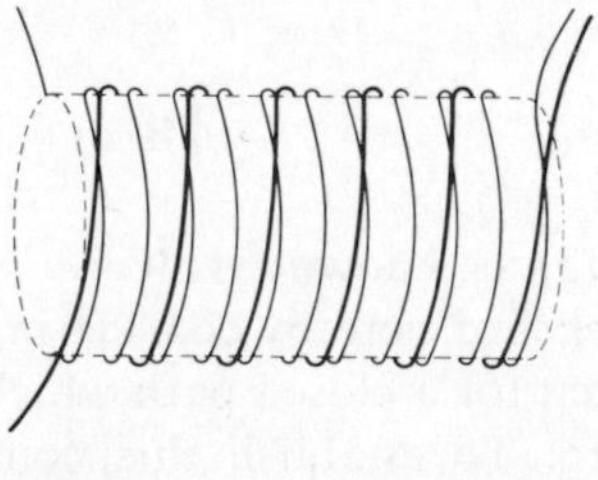

Fig. 3-12 A mutual inductance.

is

$$V = \frac{\mu_v n_1 n_2 A}{l} \frac{dI_1}{dt}$$

Hence,

$$L_{12} = \frac{\mu_v n_1 n_2 A}{l} \tag{3–71}$$

But by (3–69)

$$L_1 = \frac{\mu_v n_1^2 A}{l}, \qquad L_2 = \frac{\mu_v n_2^2 A}{l}$$

so that

$$L_{12} = \sqrt{L_1 L_2}$$

The ratio

$$k = L_{12}/\sqrt{L_1 L_2} \tag{3–72}$$

is called the *coefficient of coupling* of the mutual inductance, and for the present case—with complete coupling—$k = 1$.

3.7 The Displacement Current

We now wish to introduce the last—and most involved—of the four Maxwell equations. We start by considering a long, straight wire (Fig. 3–13) carrying a current I. The lines of induction are concentric circles, and the magnitude of **B** was shown in Example 3–2 to be given by

$$B = \frac{\mu_v I}{2\pi a} \tag{3–36}$$

If we calculate the line integral $\oint \mathbf{B} \cdot d\mathbf{l}$ around any circle of radius a, we obtain

$$\oint \mathbf{B} \cdot d\mathbf{l} = \frac{\mu_v I}{2\pi a} \int dl = \frac{\mu_v I}{2\pi a} (2\pi a)$$

or

$$\oint \mathbf{B} \cdot d\mathbf{l} = \mu_v I \tag{3–73}$$

Equation (3–73) is known as *Weber's law* or *Ampere's circuital law*, and has been established here by considering a simple, special example.

We note that for a closed path which does *not* surround the wire, the integral is zero. To establish this, consider the dashed path of Fig. 3–13.

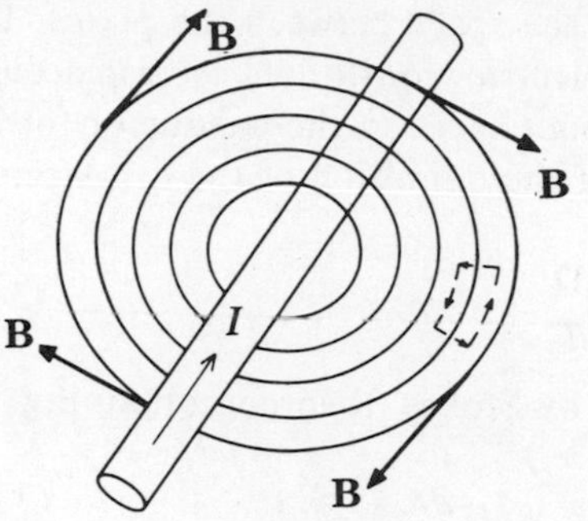

Fig. 3-13 Derivation of Weber's law.

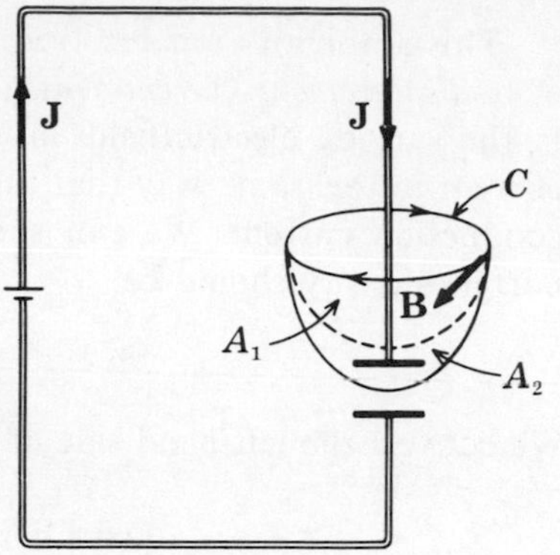

Fig. 3-14 Justification of the necessity for introducing the displacement current.

The integrals on the two circular portions of the path are equal in magnitude but opposite in sign, thus cancelling each other; for the radial portions, **B** is normal to the path, and hence, $\mathbf{B}\cdot d\mathbf{l} = 0$. Since any path can be broken down into radial and normal components, the integral vanishes if it does not go around the wire.

Problem 3-11

A long, straight line of radius R carries a uniform current I.

(a) Use Weber's law to find the induction **B** inside and outside the wire.

(b) Plot B as a function of the distance from the center of the wire.

(c) Show the geometrical relation between **J** and **B**.

If we now wish to extend Eq. (3–73) to a conductor of arbitrary shape, we use the relation

$$I = \int \mathbf{J}\cdot d\mathbf{A} \tag{3–74}$$

so that (3–73) becomes

$$\oint \mathbf{B}\cdot d\mathbf{l} = \mu_v \int \mathbf{J}\cdot d\mathbf{A} \tag{3–75}$$

Consider next the capacitor of Fig. 3–14 being charged so that a current is flowing in the circuit. If we choose a closed path C around the wire and a surface A_1 which cuts the wire, then Eq. (3–75) relates the integral around C to the integral over A_1. On the other hand, if we integrate over a surface A_2 which passes between the capacitor plates, then $\mathbf{J} = 0$ and the line integral has one of the following *two* values

$$\oint \mathbf{B}\cdot d\mathbf{l} = \begin{cases} \mu_v I \\ 0 \end{cases} \tag{3–76}$$

This ambiguity was resolved by Maxwell, who postulated the existence of a *displacement current-density* $\mathbf{J}_D$ in the space between the plates. That is, the varying electric field in the dielectric constitutes a displacement current in the same way that the moving charge in the conductor forms a conduction current. We can show that the definition of the displacement current-density should be

$$\mathbf{J}_D = \frac{\partial \mathbf{D}}{\partial t} \tag{3-77}$$

We convert the left-hand side of (3–75) by Stokes' theorem, obtaining

$$\int \textbf{curl B} \cdot d\mathbf{A} = \mu_v \int \mathbf{J}_T \cdot d\mathbf{A} \tag{3-78}$$

where we write $\mathbf{J}_T$ to indicate that we are dealing with the total current-density, that is, the sum of the conduction and displacement currents.

For an arbitrarily small element,

$$\textbf{curl B} = \mu_v \mathbf{J}_T \tag{3-79}$$

Taking the divergence of both sides gives

$$\text{div}\,\textbf{curl B} = \mu_v \,\text{div}\,\mathbf{J}_T = 0$$

or

$$\text{div}\,\mathbf{J}_T = 0 \tag{3-80}$$

Then the total current-density is the following sum

$$\mathbf{J}_T = \mathbf{J} + \mathbf{J}_D \tag{3-81}$$

Returning to the equation of continuity, Eq. (3–18), we realize that it applies only to the conduction current. However

$$\text{div}\,\mathbf{J}_D = -\text{div}\,\mathbf{J} = \frac{\partial \rho}{\partial t} = \frac{\partial}{\partial t}\,(\text{div}\,\mathbf{D}) \tag{3-82}$$

and reversing the order of differentiation verifies (3–77). If we then write (3–79) as

$$\textbf{curl B} = \mu_v\left(\mathbf{J} + \frac{\partial \mathbf{D}}{\partial t}\right) \tag{3-83}$$

we obtain the *fourth Maxwell equation*, which states that both moving charges and changing electric fields give rise to magnetic fields.

Example 3-7 Calculation of the Inductance of a Toroid from Weber's Law

Consider a toroidal coil with dimensions as shown in Fig. 3–15. We can find the inductance by starting with Weber's law

$$\oint \mathbf{B} \cdot d\mathbf{l} = \mu_v I \tag{3-73}$$

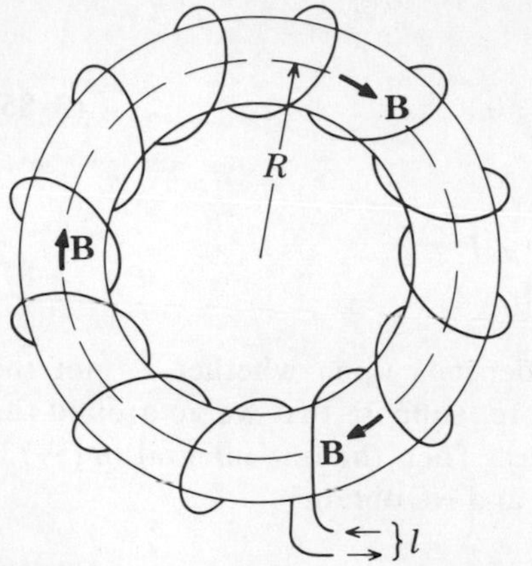

Fig. 3-15 Application of Weber's law to a toroid.

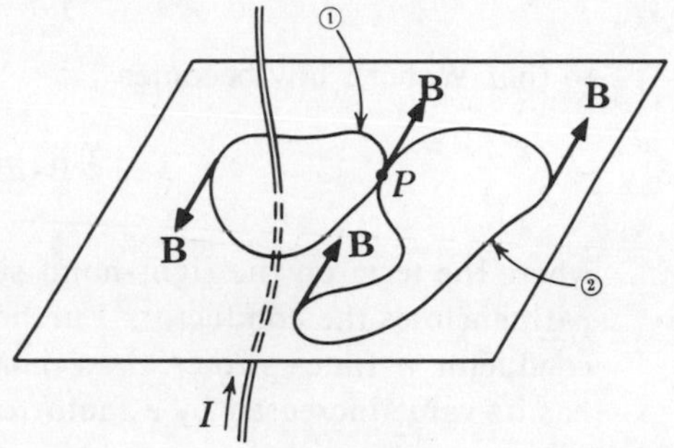

Fig. 3-16 Weber's law applied to two types of closed paths.

For a coil of n turns, this is modified to

$$\oint \mathbf{B} \cdot d\mathbf{l} = n\mu_v I \tag{3-84}$$

The lines of induction **B** inside a toroid should be parallel to the walls, by symmetry. Then the above integral becomes

$$2\pi R B = n\mu_v I$$

or

$$B = \frac{n\mu_v I}{2\pi R} \tag{3-85}$$

so that the magnetic flux is

$$\Phi = B(\pi r^2) = \frac{n\mu_v I r^2}{2R}$$

Then using the same reasoning as in Example 3–5, we obtain for the inductance

$$L = n^2 \mu_v r^2 / 2R$$

Weber's law, Eq. (3–73), implies some interesting properties of the magnetic field, and to see what these are, we must go to (3–75). Let us consider the conductor of Fig. 3–16 carrying a current I, and we choose two types of closed paths over which to evaluate the integrals in (3–75). Both paths have the same initial and terminal point P, but path number 1 encloses the wire whereas path number 2 does not. For this latter path, the surface integral must vanish, or

$$\int \mathbf{J} \cdot d\mathbf{A} = 0$$

and (3–85) becomes

$$\oint \mathbf{B}\cdot d\mathbf{l} = 0 \tag{3–86}$$

so that Weber's law becomes

$$\oint \mathbf{B}\cdot d\mathbf{l} = \begin{cases} \mu_v I \\ 0 \end{cases} \tag{3–87}$$

where the term on the right-hand side depends upon whether or not the path encloses the conductor. Furthermore, suppose that we go around the conductor n times rather than just once. Then the line integral in (3–73) has its value increased by a factor of n, and we obtain

$$\oint \mathbf{B}\cdot d\mathbf{l} = n\mu_v I \tag{3–88}$$

This equation will be taken as the complete expression for Weber's law, provided that I represents the current enclosed by the path. In this respect, this equation is analogous to Gauss' law. It differs, however, in one significant way: The magnetic field is *non-conservative*, and such a field is defined as one for which the value of the line-integral like that in Eq. (3–88) depends on the path. Hence, electrostatic fields are conservative, but magnetostatic fields are not. The origin of this term comes from the way in which energy is conserved in a field. For example, if we raise a book from the floor to a table, we could recover all the work done by letting the book fall back to the floor while coupled to a frictionless machine. Hence, in principle, a gravitational field is conservative, but in practice, it is not. A feature of conservative fields is that their properties can be expressed in terms of a scalar potential, such as the relation

$$\mathbf{E} = -\mathbf{grad}\ V \tag{1–36}$$

Since a non-conservative field must, in general, have its defining equation involve directional properties, however, the corresponding basic relation for the magnetic field is the equation

$$\mathbf{B} = \mathbf{curl}\ \mathbf{A} \tag{3–49}$$

3.8 Maxwell's Equations and the Wave Equations

Let us now collect the four Maxwell equations in one place. These were previously shown to be

$$\text{div}\ \mathbf{D} = \rho \tag{2–31}$$

$$\text{div}\ \mathbf{B} = 0 \tag{3–50}$$

$$\mathbf{curl\ E} = -\frac{\partial \mathbf{B}}{\partial t} \tag{3–62}$$

$$\mathbf{curl\ B} = \mu_v\left(\mathbf{J} + \frac{\partial \mathbf{D}}{\partial t}\right) \tag{3–83}$$

If we consider the form of these equations in free space, where $\rho = 0$ and $\mathbf{J} = 0$, we obtain*

$$\mathbf{div\ D} = 0 \tag{3–89}$$

$$\mathbf{div\ B} = 0 \tag{3–90}$$

$$\mathbf{curl\ E} = -\frac{\partial \mathbf{B}}{\partial t} \tag{3–91}$$

$$\mathbf{curl\ B} = \mu_v \frac{\partial \mathbf{D}}{\partial t} \tag{3–92}$$

Taking the curl of both sides of (3–91) gives

$$\mathbf{curl\ curl\ E} + \mathbf{curl}\frac{\partial \mathbf{B}}{\partial t} = 0 \tag{3–93}$$

Then the vector identity (A–10) converts this into the relation

$$\mathbf{grad\ div\ E} - \nabla^2\mathbf{E} + \mathbf{curl}\frac{\partial \mathbf{B}}{\partial t} = 0 \tag{3–94}$$

Substituting (3–91) and (3–92) into (3–94) then gives

$$\nabla^2\mathbf{E} = \mu_v \frac{\partial^2 \mathbf{D}}{\partial t^2} = \mu_v \epsilon_v \frac{\partial^2 \mathbf{E}}{\partial t^2} \tag{3–95}$$

where $\mathbf{D} = \epsilon_v \mathbf{E}$, and we have used the assumption that we can interchange the order of differentiation with respect to time and space coordinates, since x, y, z and t are taken as independent variables. Let us define a constant c by the relation

$$c^2 = \frac{1}{\mu_v \epsilon_v} \tag{3–96}$$

so that (3–95) becomes

$$\nabla^2\mathbf{E} = \frac{1}{c^2}\frac{\partial^2 \mathbf{E}}{\partial t^2} \tag{3–97}$$

Problem 3-12

(a) Show that c has dimensions of velocity.

(b) Show that c has a magnitude given by

$$c = 3 \times 10^8 \text{ m/sec} \tag{3–98}$$

---

*The equations involving **B** can also be expressed in terms of **H** via the relation $\mathbf{B} = \mu_v \mathbf{H}$, where μ_v and **H** are analogous to ϵ_v and **E**, respectively, in the expression $\mathbf{D} = \epsilon_v \mathbf{E}$. We shall define and discuss μ_v and **H** in the next chapter.

The relation expressed by Eq. (3–98) indicates that c can be identified with the velocity of propagation of light in free space. Equation (3–97), known as the *wave equation*, predicts that the electric field will be propagated in free space with a velocity c. To see why this equation describes the motion of a wave, let us assume that $\mathbf{E}$ is a function of z only. That is, we let

$$\mathbf{E} = \mathbf{E}(z, t) \tag{3–99}$$

and (3–97) reduces to the form

$$\frac{\partial^2 \mathbf{E}}{\partial z^2} = \frac{1}{c^2}\frac{\partial^2 \mathbf{E}}{\partial t^2} \tag{3–100}$$

We would now like to show that Eq. (3–100) is the equation of a wave moving along the z-axis with a velocity c. To do this, consider a long piece of wire bent into the shape of a cosine curve and oriented as shown in Fig. 3–17. This curve has the equation

$$x = a\cos kz \tag{3–101}$$

where a is the *amplitude* of the curve, and k is a quantity to be determined.

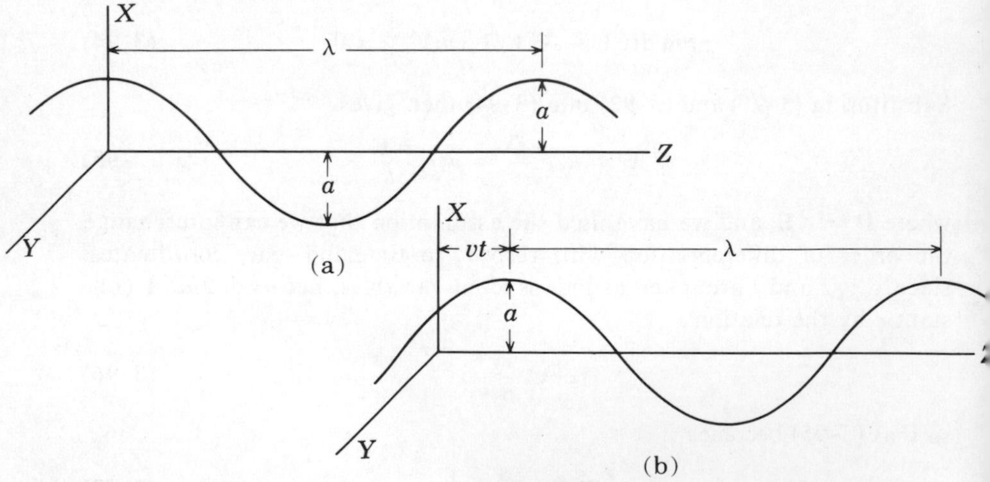

Fig. 3-17 A cosine wave.

The distance between the two maxima on the curve is the wavelength λ, and when $z = 0$ or λ, then $x = a$. Hence,

$$k\lambda = 2\pi$$

or

$$k = \frac{2\pi}{\lambda} \tag{3–102}$$

and

$$x = a \cos\left(\frac{2\pi}{\lambda}\right) \tag{3–103}$$

The quantity k is called the *propagation constant* or *wave number*, and by (3–102) it is proportional to the number of waves/meter in the field being propagated. Now let the rigid curve move to the right with a velocity v (Fig. 3–17b). At a time t, the entire curve will have moved a distance vt, and Eq. (3–101) is modified to

$$x = a \cos\left[\frac{2\pi}{\lambda}(x - vt)\right] \tag{3–104}$$

Problem 3-13

(a) Verify that Eq. (3–104) describes a cosine wave moving to the right with velocity v.

(b) Show that Eq. (3–104) satisfies the partial differential equations

$$v^2 \frac{\partial^2 x}{\partial z^2} = \frac{\partial^2 x}{\partial t^2} \tag{3–105}$$

This equation will be recognized as having the form of (3–97), and we therefore see that the electric field is a wave propagated along the z-direction with the vector **E** normal to the direction of propagation. Using the same procedure, it can be shown that a similar equation holds for the magnetic field. This equation is

$$\nabla^2 \mathbf{B} = \frac{1}{c^2}\frac{\partial^2 \mathbf{B}}{\partial t^2} \tag{3–106}$$

A solution of (3–97) can be seen from (3–104) to have the form

$$\mathbf{E} = \mathbf{E}_m \cos\left[\frac{2\pi}{\lambda}(z - vt)\right] \tag{3–107}$$

where $\mathbf{E}_m$ is the amplitude of **E**. It is convenient to reintroduce k into (3–107). We also use

$$f = \frac{\omega}{2\pi} \tag{3–108}$$

and

$$v = \lambda f = \frac{\lambda\omega}{2\pi} \tag{3–109}$$

where f is the frequency of the wave and ω is the angular frequency. Then (3–107) becomes

$$\mathbf{E} = \mathbf{E}_m \cos(kz - \omega t) \tag{3–110}$$

The relation

$$e^{ix} = \cos x + i \sin x$$

would lead us to believe that the solution (3–110) of the wave equation can also be put in the exponential form

$$\mathbf{E} = \mathbf{E}_m e^{i(kz-\omega t)} \tag{3–111}$$

Problem 3-14

Verify that (3–111) satisfies

$$\frac{\partial^2 \mathbf{E}}{\partial z^2} = \frac{1}{c^2}\frac{\partial^2 \mathbf{E}}{\partial t^2} \tag{3–97}$$

We can extend this solution to three dimensions by introducing a *propagation vector* of the form

$$\mathbf{k} = k_x\mathbf{i} + k_y\mathbf{j} + k_z\mathbf{k} \tag{3–112}$$

where k_z now represents the k used in Eq. (3–111) and defined by (3–102). [*NOTE:* The symbol **k** has two different meanings in Eq. (3–112), but this situation occurs so infrequently that it is not necessary to use new symbols.]

Problem 3-15

Verify that the solution to the three-dimensional wave equation

$$\nabla^2 \mathbf{E} = \frac{1}{c^2}\frac{\partial^2 \mathbf{E}}{\partial t^2} \tag{3–97}$$

is

$$\mathbf{E} = \mathbf{E}_m e^{i(\mathbf{k}\cdot\mathbf{r}-\omega t)} \tag{3–113}$$

The solution (3–113) represents a *plane wave* in free space. That is, the surfaces of *constant phase* are planes normal to the direction of propagation.

Let us utilize the fact that $\cos(-x) = \cos x$, and write an exponential solution

$$\mathbf{E} = \mathbf{E}_m e^{-i(kz-\omega t)} \tag{3–114}$$

in place of (3–111). Comparing this with (3–113), we see that $\mathbf{k}\cdot\mathbf{r}$ represents the phase of the wave. To show now that it is a plane wave, we consider the surfaces defined by the equation

$$\mathbf{k}\cdot\mathbf{r} = C \tag{3–115}$$

where C is a constant. This relation defines a plane normal to **k** and lying a distance $r \cos\theta$ from the vertex of the angle θ (Fig. 3–18). Hence, the surfaces of constant phase for the solution (3–113) are planes, and these planes move with a velocity c, which is consequently known as the *phase velocity*.

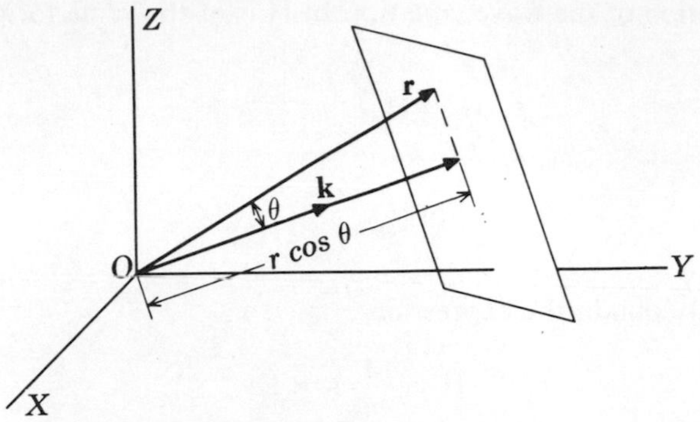

Fig. 3-18 A plane of constant phase.

Turning now to the Maxwell equation (3–91), we obtain the relation

$$\mathbf{curl\ E} = -\mu_v \frac{\partial \mathbf{H}}{\partial t} \tag{3–116}$$

using $\mathbf{B} = \mu_v \mathbf{H}$. Hence, the propagation of a sinusoidal electric field implies the existence of an associated magnetic field. To see the relation between **E** and **H**, we substitute (3–113) into (3–116), obtaining

$$e^{-i\omega t}\ \mathbf{curl}\ (\mathbf{E}_m e^{i\cdot\mathbf{kr}}) = -\mu_v \frac{\partial \mathbf{H}}{\partial t} \tag{3–117}$$

where we have again used the fact that the space and time variables are independent. Expanding the curl through the use of the identity (A–4) and noting that $\mathbf{E}_m$ is a constant gives

$$\mathbf{curl}\ (\mathbf{E}_m e^{i\mathbf{k}\cdot\mathbf{r}}) = (\mathbf{grad}\ e^{i\mathbf{k}\cdot\mathbf{r}}) \times \mathbf{E}_m \tag{3–118}$$

Problem 3-16

Show that

$$\mathbf{grad}\ e^{i\mathbf{k}\cdot\mathbf{r}} = i\mathbf{k}e^{i\mathbf{k}\cdot\mathbf{r}} \tag{3–119}$$

We now define *Poynting's vector* **P** by

$$\mathbf{P} = \mathbf{E} \times \mathbf{H} \tag{3–120}$$

Problem 3-17

Show that Poynting's vector has dimensions of watts/meter^2.

Hence, the Poynting vector represents the power carried by the plane wave. That is, it can be thought of as a sort of power vector, although power is normally a scalar quantity. Returning now to Eq. (3–117), it then becomes

$$i\mathbf{k} \times \mathbf{E}_m e^{-(i\mathbf{k}\cdot\mathbf{r}-\omega t)} = i\mathbf{k} \times \mathbf{E} = -\mu_v \frac{\partial \mathbf{H}}{\partial t} \tag{3–121}$$

The solution of the wave equation in **H** is of the same form as (3–113), namely,

$$\mathbf{H} = \mathbf{H}_m e^{-(i\mathbf{k}\cdot\mathbf{r}-\omega t)} \tag{3–122}$$

so that

$$\frac{\partial \mathbf{H}}{\partial t} = -i\omega \mathbf{H} \tag{3–123}$$

and we finally obtain the expression

$$\mathbf{H} = \frac{1}{\omega\mu_v}\mathbf{k} \times \mathbf{E} \tag{3–124}$$

which shows that **k**, **E**, and **H** form a right-handed set of mutually orthogonal vectors; that is, **E** and **H** lie perpendicular to one another in the planes of constant phase, as shown in Fig. 3–19.

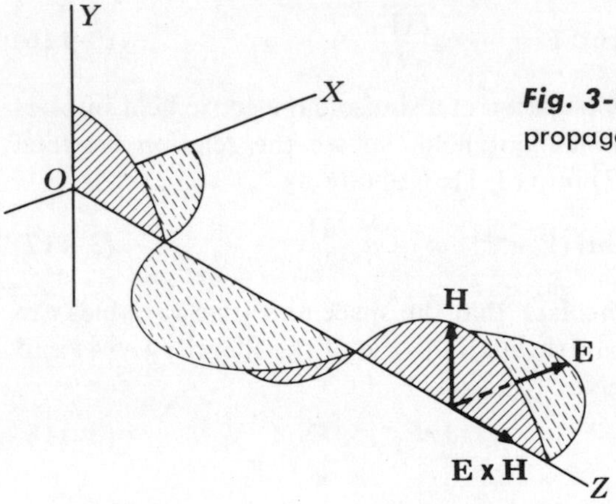

Fig. 3-19 Relation of field vectors to propagation direction in a plane wave.

If we let $\mathbf{k}_0$ be a unit vector along **k**, then (3–124) becomes

$$\mathbf{H} = \left(\frac{k}{\omega\mu_v}\right)\mathbf{k}_0 \times \mathbf{E}$$

By (3–109) and (3–102), the velocity c can be expressed as

$$c = \frac{\omega}{k} \tag{3–125}$$

and by (4–165), we have

$$\frac{\omega}{k} = \frac{1}{\sqrt{\epsilon_v \mu_v}} \tag{3–126}$$

Hence, (3–124) becomes

$$\sqrt{\frac{\mu_v}{\epsilon_v}}\,\mathbf{H} = \mathbf{k}_0 \times \mathbf{E} \tag{3–127}$$

Problem 3-18

(a) Prove that $\sqrt{\mu_v/\epsilon_v}$ has dimensions of ohms.

(b) Show that the value of $\sqrt{\mu_v/\epsilon_v}$ is approximately 377 ohms.

This quantity, whose value is approximately 377 ohms, is called the *characteristic impedance of free space.*

If we now take the scalar product of Eq. (4–160) with **H** and subtract from it the scalar product of (4–161) with **E**, we obtain

$$\begin{aligned}\mathbf{H}\cdot\mathbf{curl}\,\mathbf{E} - \mathbf{E}\cdot\mathbf{curl}\,\mathbf{H} \\ = -\left(\mathbf{H}\cdot\frac{\partial\mathbf{B}}{\partial t} + \mathbf{E}\cdot\frac{\partial\mathbf{D}}{\partial t}\right) \\ = -\frac{\partial}{\partial t}\left(\frac{\mu_v H^2}{2} + \frac{\epsilon_v E^2}{2}\right)\end{aligned} \qquad \textbf{(3–128)}$$

From (A–6) we see that

$$\mathrm{div}\,(\mathbf{E}\times\mathbf{H}) = \mathbf{H}\cdot\mathbf{curl}\,\mathbf{E} - \mathbf{E}\cdot\mathbf{curl}\,\mathbf{H} \qquad \textbf{(3–129)}$$

The right-hand side of (3–128) in accordance with Eq. (3–123), represents the energy-density or energy W_V per unit volume associated with the electric field; and similarly, we would expect $\mu_v H^2/2$ to be the corresponding quantity for the magnetic field. Hence, the quantity in parentheses represents the total energy-density associated with the wave. Combining this fact with (3–128) and (3–120) then shows that

$$\mathrm{div}\,\mathbf{P} + \frac{\partial W_V}{\partial t} = 0 \qquad \textbf{(3–130)}$$

which is known as *Poynting's theorem.* It will be recognized as having the form of the continuity equation (3–18), and is, in fact, one of many forms of this equation which we encounter in engineering and science.

Problem 3-19

Show that the Poynting vector for a plane wave is

$$\mathbf{P} = \mathbf{k}_0 E^2\sqrt{\frac{\epsilon_v}{\mu_v}} \qquad (3\text{-}131)$$

Equation (3–131) can be regarded as a form of Ohm's law for free space. The power dissipated in a resistance R by a current I is given by

$$P = VI \qquad \textbf{(3–132)}$$

since V represents the work per unit charge required to transport the charge in the circuit, and I is the amount of charge moved per unit time. By (3–3), this can be written

$$P = \frac{V^2}{R} \qquad \textbf{(3–133)}$$

Comparing (3–131) and (3–133) and noting the result of Problem 3–18, we see the similarity.

3.9 Boundary Conditions for Electromagnetic Fields

The requirements imposed on a static electric field at the interface between two different dielectric materials were discussed in Chap. 2, and it was shown there that these boundary conditions could be expressed by the relations

$$D_{n1} - D_{n2} = \sigma \tag{2-53}$$

and

$$E_{t1} = E_{t2} \tag{2-56}$$

We would now like to examine the validity of these boundary conditions for time-varying fields as well as finding the corresponding relations for **B** and **H**.

Figure 3–20a shows the interface between medium 1 and medium 2, with a Gaussian surface of cylindrical shape lying across the boundary. The conductivity of each medium is denoted by σ, the dielectric coefficient by ϵ_r, and an analogous magnetic property—the *relative permeability*—by μ_r. We will give a definition of μ_r in the next chapter and, for the time being, will simply use it to indicate that the two media have different magnetic properties.

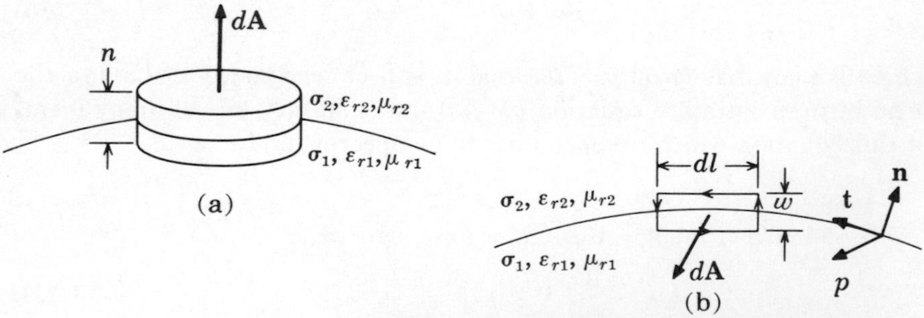

Fig. 3-20 Boundary conditions for electromagnetic waves.

Since the Maxwell equation (2–31) is valid for static or varying fields in a material medium, then Gauss' law is similarly valid; the procedure of Chap. 2 verifies the relation

$$\oint \mathbf{D} \cdot d\mathrm{A} = (D_{1n} - D_{2n})dA = \sigma$$

or

$$D_{1n} - D_{2n} = \sigma \tag{3-134}$$

which is the same as (2–53). A similar procedure, when applied to the relation

$$\oint \mathbf{B} \cdot d\mathbf{A} = 0 \tag{3–51}$$

gives the corresponding boundary condition

$$B_{1n} - B_{2n} = 0 \tag{3–135}$$

showing that the normal component of **B** is continuous.

Now we replace the cylinder by the rectangular path of surface area dA shown in Fig. 3–20b. Using Faraday's law

$$\oint \mathbf{E} \cdot d\mathbf{l} = \frac{-\partial}{\partial t} \int \mathbf{B} \cdot d\mathbf{A} \tag{3–136}$$

and making the ends of the path very small, we can write

$$(\mathbf{E}_1 - \mathbf{E}_2) \cdot \mathbf{t}\, dl + \frac{\partial \mathbf{B}}{\partial t} \cdot \mathbf{p}\, dA = 0 \tag{3–137}$$

where **t** is a unit vector tangential to the interface, **n** is a unit normal vector, and **p** is a third unit vector perpendicular to both **t** and **n**. Then **p**, **n**, and **t** form a right-handed system, and

$$\mathbf{t} = \mathbf{p} \times \mathbf{n}$$

so that

$$(\mathbf{E}_1 - \mathbf{E}_2) \cdot \mathbf{t} = \mathbf{t} \cdot (\mathbf{E}_1 - \mathbf{E}_2) = \mathbf{p} \cdot \mathbf{n} \times (\mathbf{E}_1 - \mathbf{E}_2)$$

The quantity $d\mathbf{A}$ on the left-hand side of (3–137) will approach zero as we let the ends of the path get very small, and the above equation then reduces to

$$\mathbf{n} \times (\mathbf{E}_1 - \mathbf{E}_2) = 0$$

or

$$E_{1t} - E_{2t} = 0 \tag{3–138}$$

Thus, (2–56) is valid in the presence of a magnetic field which may be steady or time-varying.

Turning now to the fourth Maxwell equation, which is

$$\mathbf{curl\, H} = \mathbf{J} + \frac{\partial \mathbf{D}}{\partial t} \tag{3–83}$$

we multiply both sides by $d\mathbf{A} = \mathbf{p}\, dA$ and integrate to obtain

$$\int \mathbf{curl\, H} \cdot \mathbf{p}\, dA = \int \mathbf{J} \cdot \mathbf{p}\, dA + \int \frac{\partial \mathbf{D}}{\partial t} \cdot \mathbf{p}\, dA$$

Then by Stokes' theorem,

$$\oint \mathbf{H} \cdot d\mathbf{l} = \int \mathbf{J} \cdot \mathbf{p}\, dA + \int \frac{\partial \mathbf{D}}{\partial t} \cdot \mathbf{p}\, dA \tag{3–139}$$

Before we can examine what happens to (3–139) as dA gets vanishingly small, we must introduce the concept of *surface current density* $\mathbf{J}_A$. Suppose that we take a thin section of a conductor carrying a current density $\mathbf{J}$ (Fig. 3–21). We then define the surface current as the value which $\mathbf{J}$ approaches when we make this section thinner, without changing the value of the current I. We note that this process makes $\mathbf{J}$ increase. since we are putting the same current into a smaller volume. Hence, our definition can be expressed analytically by the relation

$$\mathbf{J}_A = \lim_{\substack{w \to 0 \\ J \to \infty}} \mathbf{J}w \tag{3–140}$$

and we note that $\mathbf{J}_A$ has dimensions of amperes/meter.

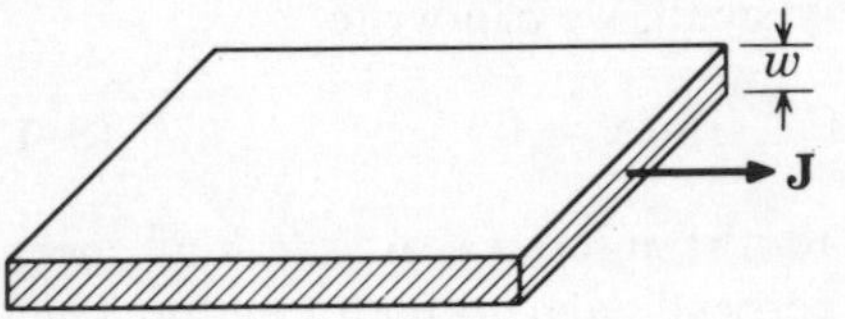

Fig. 3-21 Surface current density.

Returning to Eq. (3–139), the left-hand side is transformed as in (3–137), and the second term on the right vanishes as the ends of the path get smaller. However, the first term can be rewritten as

$$\int \mathbf{J} \cdot \mathbf{p}\,dA = \int \mathbf{J}_A \cdot \mathbf{p}\,dl$$

and we obtain

$$\mathbf{n} \times (\mathbf{H}_1 - \mathbf{H}_2) = \mathbf{J}_A$$

or

$$H_{1t} - H_{2t} = J_A \tag{3–141}$$

This equation can be considered to be the analogue of (3–134), and we note that it is strictly true only for regions of infinite conductivity, since this is the only way we can get $\mathbf{J}$ to be infinite for a finite electric field.

Example 3-8 *Two-Section Conductor*

A conducting slab with an applied potential difference is composed of two different materials as shown in Fig. 3–22. It is desired to find the electrostatic potential and surface charge at the interface. The potential across the entire conductor can be expressed as

$$V = aE_1 + bE_2 \tag{3–142}$$

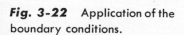

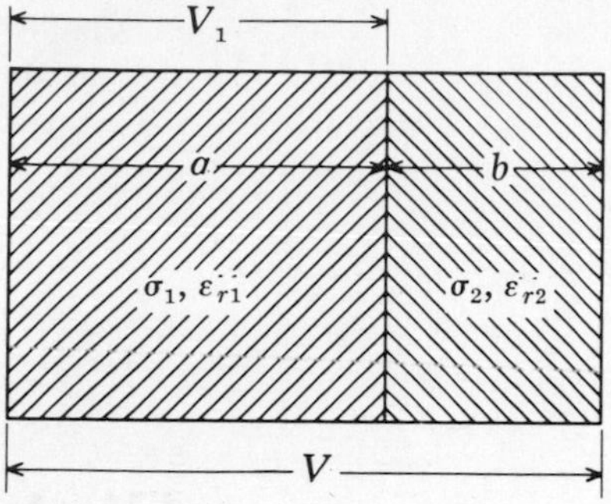

Fig. 3-22 Application of the boundary conditions.

We can also relate $\mathbf{E}_1$ and $\mathbf{E}_2$ via the boundary condition

$$D_{1n} - D_{2n} = \sigma \qquad \textbf{(3–143)}$$

or

$$\sigma = \epsilon_{r1}\epsilon_v E_1 - \epsilon_{r2}\epsilon_v E_2$$

Another relation comes from the fact that

$$J_1 = J_2$$

or

$$\sigma_1 E_1 = \sigma_2 E_2$$

Eliminating E_1 and E_2 from these three equations gives

$$\sigma = V\epsilon_v \frac{\epsilon_{r2}\sigma_1 - \epsilon_{r1}\sigma_2}{a\sigma_2 + b\sigma_1}$$

and

$$V_1 = aE_1 = \frac{Va\sigma_2}{a\sigma_2 + b\sigma_1}$$

4 Fields in Magnetic Materials

4.1 The Equivalent Current Concept

The last major topic to be covered in our study of electromagnetic theory is an extension of the theory of magnetic fields to regions containing magnetic media. This discussion will parallel to a certain extent the one of Chapter 2 for electrostatic fields, but there are also some important differences which we shall emphasize. The magnetic fields we studied in the last chapter were regarded as being entirely due to the existence of currents in conductors. However, it is known that magnetic forces can be enhanced by the presence of certain materials, such as the iron core of an electromagnet. The resultant field **B** can then be written as

$$\mathbf{B} = \mathbf{B}_I + \mathbf{B}_M \tag{4–1}$$

where $\mathbf{B}_I$ is the field due to the current and $\mathbf{B}_M$ represents the additional field coming from the magnetic medium. In this equation, we have used **B** to specify the magnetic field strength since **B** is a measure of the force on a moving charge, via Eq. (3–35), in the same way that **E** is a measure of the force on a static charge. We would now like to express $\mathbf{B}_M$ in terms of the properties of the magnetic material, and we can do this by considering the vector potential **A** of a current loop. Such a loop is shown in Fig. 4–1, and the vector potential at a point with position-vector $\mathbf{r}'(x', y', z')$ is given by the expression

$$\mathbf{A}(x', y', z') = \frac{\mu_v I}{4\pi} \oint \frac{d\mathbf{l}}{r} \tag{3–47}$$

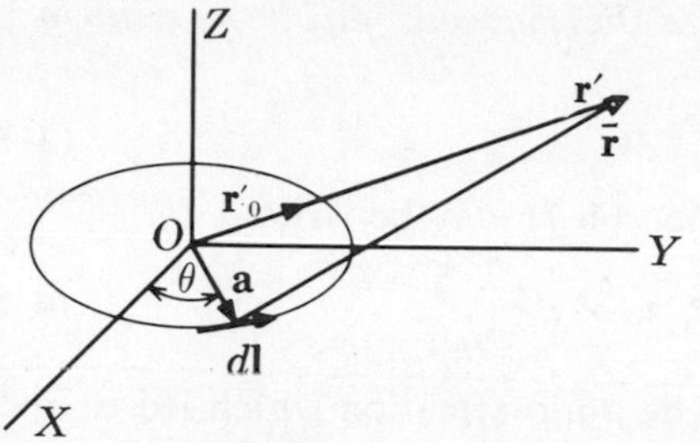

Fig. 4-1 Determination of the field at a long distance from a current-loop.

Regarding the radius of the loop as a vector **a**, we can write

$$\mathbf{r}' = \mathbf{a} + \bar{\mathbf{r}} \tag{4–2}$$

or

$$\bar{\mathbf{r}} = \mathbf{r}' - \mathbf{a}$$

and

$$\bar{r}_x = x' - a\cos\theta$$
$$\bar{r}_y = y' - a\sin\theta$$
$$\bar{r}_z = z'$$

The magnitude of $\bar{\mathbf{r}}$ is then given by

$$\bar{r} = [(x' - a\cos\theta)^2 + (y' - a\sin\theta)^2 + z'^2]^{1/2}$$
$$= [r'^2 - 2ax'\cos\theta - 2ay'\sin\theta + a^2]^{1/2}$$

and

$$\frac{1}{\bar{r}} = \frac{1}{r'\left[1 - \frac{2a}{r'^2}(x'\cos\theta + y'\sin\theta) + \frac{a^2}{r'^2}\right]^{1/2}} \tag{4–3}$$

If we assume that we are computing **A** at a distance $\bar{\mathbf{r}}$, which is large compared to the radius of the loop, then the term a^2/r'^2 in (4–3) can be dropped, and the remainder of the denominator can be expanded by the binomial theorem to give

$$\frac{1}{\bar{r}} = \frac{1}{r'}\left[1 + \frac{a}{r'^2}(x'\cos\theta + y'\sin\theta)\right] \tag{4–4}$$

If we write $d\mathbf{l}$ in component form, we see that it can be expressed as

$$d\mathbf{l} = (-a\cos\theta\mathbf{i} + a\sin\theta\mathbf{j})\,d\theta \tag{4–5}$$

Substituting (4–4) and (4–5) into (~~4–1~~ 3-47) gives

$$\mathbf{A} = \frac{\mu_v I}{4\pi}\int_0^{2\pi}\left[\frac{1}{r'} + \frac{a}{r'^3}(x'\cos\theta + y'\sin\theta)\right]a(-\sin\theta\mathbf{i} + \cos\theta\mathbf{j})\,d\theta \tag{4–6}$$

Working out the integral, we find that

$$\mathbf{A} = \frac{\mu_v I\pi a^2}{4\pi r'^3}(-\mathbf{i}y' + \mathbf{j}x') \tag{4–7}$$

Problem 4-1

Verify (4-7)

We now define a quantity known as the *magnetic dipole moment* **m** of the loop by the relation

$$\mathbf{m} = IA\mathbf{k} \tag{4-8}$$

where $A = \pi a^2$ is the surface area. Then (4–7) may be written

$$\mathbf{A} = \frac{\mu_v}{4\pi r'^2}\mathbf{m} \times \mathbf{r}_0' \tag{4-9}$$

where $\mathbf{r}_0'$ is a unit vector along $\mathbf{r}'$. The approximation which led to (4–9) will be referred to as the *dipole approximation.*

We would now like to show that the magnetic dipole moment as defined by (4–8) is analogous to the electric dipole moment **p** of Sec. 2.2. The electrostatic potential at the point (x', y', z') due to a dipole at the origin was shown to be

$$V = \frac{\mathbf{p}\cdot\mathbf{r}_0'}{4\pi\epsilon_v r'^2} \tag{2-8}$$

so that

$$\mathbf{E} = -\mathbf{grad}'V = \frac{1}{4\pi\epsilon_v}\mathbf{grad}'\left[\mathbf{p}\cdot\mathbf{grad}'\left(\frac{1}{r'}\right)\right] \tag{4-10}$$

using (2–19) with the source-point located at the origin.

Now, let us evaluate the expression

$$\mathbf{B} = \mathbf{curl}'\,\mathbf{A} \tag{3-48}$$

using (4–9), which we convert into

$$\mathbf{A} = \frac{-\mu_v}{4\pi}\mathbf{m} \times \mathbf{grad}'\left(\frac{1}{r'}\right) \tag{4-11}$$

by (2–20). Since **m** is a constant, the identity (A–4) means that

$$\mathbf{m} \times \mathbf{grad}'\left(\frac{1}{r'}\right) = \mathbf{curl}'\left(\frac{\mathbf{m}}{r'}\right)$$

Therefore,

$$\mathbf{B} = \mathbf{curl}'\,\mathbf{A} = \frac{\mu_v}{4\pi}\mathbf{curl}'\,\mathbf{curl}'\left(\frac{\mathbf{m}}{r}\right) \tag{4-12}$$

We evaluate this expression by the identity (A–10) followed by (A–3) to obtain

$$\mathbf{B} = \frac{\mu_v}{4\pi}\mathbf{grad}'\,\mathrm{div}'\left(\frac{\mathbf{m}}{r'}\right) = \frac{\mu_v}{4\pi}\mathbf{grad}'\left[\mathbf{m}\cdot\mathbf{grad}'\left(\frac{1}{r'}\right)\right] \tag{4-13}$$

since **m** is a constant and $\nabla'^2(1/r') = 0$ when $r' \neq 0$. This result has the same form as (4–10), and shows why the magnetic dipole moment **m** of a loop is defined in accordance with Eq. (4–8).

Problem 4-2

(a) Starting with Eqs. (4-11) and (3-48), show that the expression (4-13) for the field of a dipole can be written in the alternate form

$$\mathbf{B} = \frac{\mu_v}{4\pi}\left[-\frac{\mathbf{m}}{r'^3} + \frac{3(\mathbf{m}\cdot\mathbf{r}')\mathbf{r}'}{r'^5}\right] \qquad \textbf{(4-14)}$$

(b) Show that the expression (3–37) for the field on the axis of a circular coil gives the same result as (4-14) for distances which are large compared with the radius of the coil.

(c) Show that the equation giving the field **B** due to a dipole of moment **m** is

$$\mathbf{B} = \frac{\mu_v m}{4\pi r^3}(2\cos\theta\,\mathbf{i}_r + \sin\theta\,\mathbf{i}_\theta) \qquad \textbf{(4-15)}$$

and that this result agrees with (4-14).

It is interesting to compare the fields due to an electric and magnetic dipole. Figure 4–2a shows the electric field due to two equal but opposite point-charges; Fig. 4–2b shows the magnetic induction due to a current-loop. We see that at a distance large compared with the dimensions of the source, the two are identical.

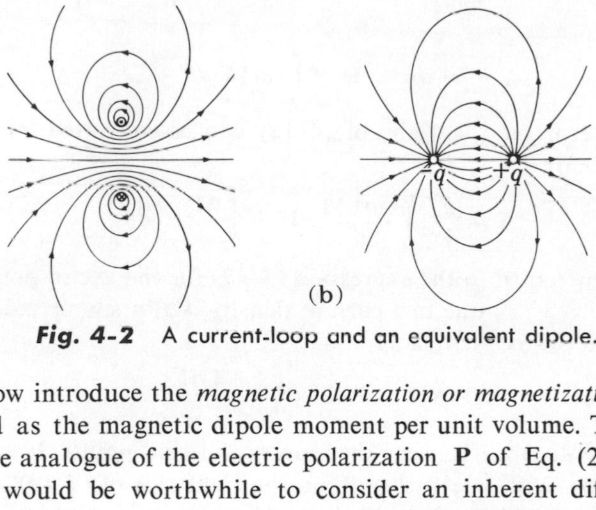

(a) (b)

Fig. 4-2 A current-loop and an equivalent dipole.

We now introduce the *magnetic polarization or magnetization* **M**, which is defined as the magnetic dipole moment per unit volume. This quantity is then the analogue of the electric polarization **P** of Eq. (2–11). At this point, it would be worthwhile to consider an inherent difficulty in the definition of either type of polarization. Let us consider a small volume element ΔV which contains a large, but finite, number of distinct dipoles. The moment of this volume is

$$\Delta\mathbf{m} = \sum_{\Delta V} \mathbf{m}_i$$

where the $\mathbf{m}_i$ are the moments of the individual dipoles. The average polarization is then

$$<\mathbf{M}> = \frac{\Delta\mathbf{m}}{\Delta V}$$

and the polarization at a given point is obtained by shrinking ΔV so that it approaches this point as a limit. That is,

$$\mathbf{M} = \lim_{\Delta V\to 0} <\mathbf{M}> = \frac{d\mathbf{m}}{dV} \qquad \textbf{(4–16)}$$

In carrying out this limiting process, we are assuming that the dipoles are not discrete entities but form a continuous distribution. Equation (4–16) is then based on the validity of this assumption, so that we require ΔV to be small, yet large enough to contain enough dipoles to give a true picture of the dipole-density at any point in the material.

The vector potential due to a body whose polarization is **M** can be expressed as

$$\mathbf{A} = \frac{\mu_v}{4\pi}\int \frac{\mathbf{M} \times \mathbf{r}'_0}{r'^2}dV \tag{4–17}$$

by (4–9) and (4–16). Now using the relation

$$-\,\mathbf{grad}\left(\frac{1}{r'}\right) = \frac{\mathbf{r}'_0}{r'^2} = \frac{\mathbf{r}'}{r'^3} \tag{2–19}$$

and also using the vector identity, (A–4), this becomes

$$\mathbf{A} = \frac{\mu_v}{4\pi}\left[\int \frac{\mathbf{curl\ M}}{r'}\,dV - \int \mathbf{curl}\left(\frac{\mathbf{M}}{r'}\right)dV\right] \tag{4–18}$$

Using

$$\oint d\mathbf{A} \times \mathbf{F} = \int \mathbf{curl\ F}\,dV \tag{A–13}$$

the second term on the right of (4–18) can be converted into a surface integral to obtain

$$\mathbf{A} = \frac{\mu_v}{4\pi}\left[\int \frac{\mathbf{curl\ M}}{r'}\,dV + \oint \frac{\mathbf{M}}{r'} \times d\mathbf{A}\right] \tag{4–19}$$

Let us now return to the expression (3–47) for the vector potential **A** at a field-point (x', y', z') due to a current density **J** at a source point (x, y, z). This equation can be written as

$$\mathbf{A}(x', y', z') = \frac{\mu_v}{4\pi}\int \frac{\mathbf{J}\,dV}{\bar{r}} \tag{4–20}$$

where $\bar{r}$ is the distance between the source- and field-points. If we compare this expression with the first term on the right side of (4–19), we can say that the magnetic material establishes a vector potential which is partially due to an *equivalent volume current-density* or *Amperian current-density* $\mathbf{J}_M$ given by

$$\mathbf{J}_M = \mathbf{curl\ M} \tag{4–21}$$

Equation (4–20) corresponds directly to the first term of (4–19), since r' is the distance between the field-point and the location of the dipole equivalent to the current-loop. It is important to realize that this current $\mathbf{J}_M$ is *not* a real current; it is a fictitious current which enables us to calculate —in part—the vector potential due to a magnetized material with dipole density **M**. Similarly, the second term in (4–19) can be regarded as defining an *Amperian surface current-density* $\mathbf{J}_{MA}$ given by

$$\mathbf{J}_{MA} = \mathbf{M} \times \mathbf{n} \tag{4–22}$$

where we have used the definition (3–140) for $\mathbf{J}_{MA}$ and where

$$d\mathbf{A} = \mathbf{n}\, dA$$

We have thus solved the problem posed at the beginning of this section; the magnetic induction $\mathbf{B}_M$ due to the presence of the magnetic material is given by

$$\mathbf{B}_M = \mathbf{curl}\ \mathbf{A}_M \tag{4–23}$$

where

$$\mathbf{A}_M = \frac{\mu_v}{4\pi}\left[\int \frac{\mathbf{J}_M}{r'}\, dV + \oint \frac{\mathbf{J}_{MA}}{r'}\, dA\right] \tag{4–24}$$

Going back to the relation (3–48), we see that

$$\mathbf{B}_M = \mathbf{curl}'\ \mathbf{A}_M = \frac{\mu_v}{4\pi}\left[\int \mathbf{curl}'\left(\frac{\mathbf{J}_M}{r'}\right) dV + \oint \mathbf{curl}'\left(\frac{\mathbf{J}_{MA}}{r'}\right) dA\right] \tag{4–25}$$

where the order of differentiation and integration has been interchanged. Using the identity (A–4) and the fact that $\mathbf{curl}'\ \mathbf{J}_M = 0$ and $\mathbf{curl}\ \mathbf{J}_{MA} = 0$, since $\mathbf{J}_{MA}$ is a function only of x, y and z, we obtain

$$\mathbf{B}_M = \frac{\mu_v}{4\pi}\left[\int \frac{\mathbf{J}_M \times \mathbf{r}_0'}{r'^2}\, dV + \frac{\mu_0}{4\pi}\oint \frac{\mathbf{J}_{MA} \times \mathbf{r}_0'}{r'^2}\, dA\right] \tag{4–26}$$

The two terms on the right correspond to the definition of $\mathbf{B}$ as given by (3–34), so that (4–26) could have been written down immediately, had we postulated the existence of the equivalent or Amperian currents.

Problem 4-3

A disc is magnetized uniformly perpendicular to its faces. Find the field $\mathbf{B}$ at a point on the axis outside the disc, and show that your answer agrees with problem 3-5a.

4.2 Fields Inside Magnetic Materials

We would now like to consider in more detail the internal fields for magnetic media. Let us therefore calculate $\mathbf{B}_M$ inside the arbitrary body of Fig. 4–3. To do this, we choose some interior point P and draw a sphere of radius R centered on P. We choose R large enough so that the dipole approximation of the previous section is applicable. The value of $\mathbf{B}$ at the center of the sphere is then the sum of four terms: the contributions at P due to the two volumes V' and V'' and the two surfaces S and S'. By (4–26), then, we have the following expression for the internal field:

$$\mathbf{B}_M = \frac{\mu_v}{4\pi}\int \frac{\mathbf{J}_M \times \mathbf{r}_0'}{r'^2}\, dV' + \frac{\mu_v}{4\pi}\oint \frac{\mathbf{J}_{MA} \times \mathbf{r}_0'}{r'^2}\, dA$$
$$+ \mathbf{B}_V'' + \frac{\mu_v}{4\pi}\oint \frac{\mathbf{J}_{MA} \times \mathbf{r}_0'}{r'^2}\, dA' \tag{4–27}$$

where $\mathbf{B}_V''$ is the contribution to $\mathbf{B}_M$ from the equivalent volume current inside the sphere.

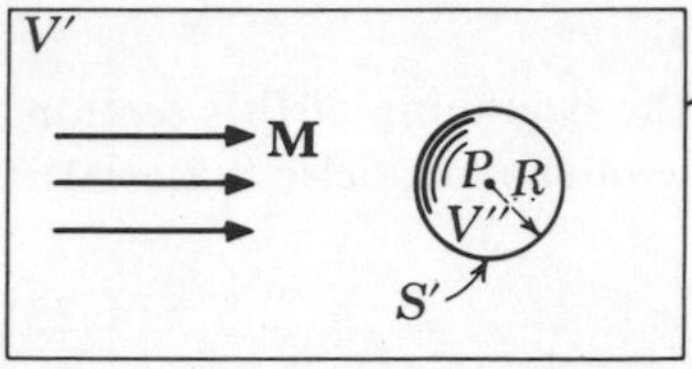

Fig. 4-3 An internal field expressed in terms of Amperian currents.

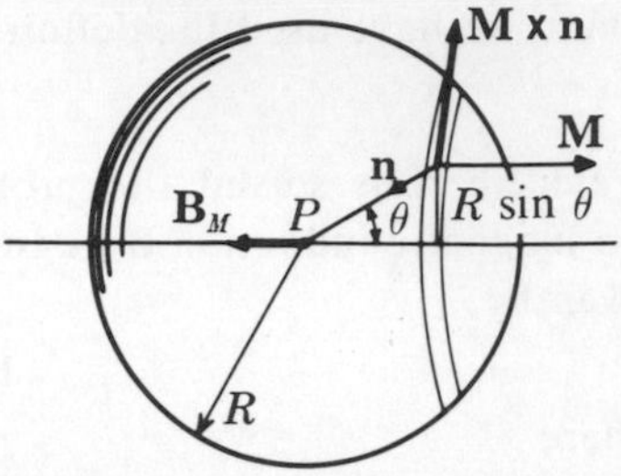

Fig. 4-4 The spherical cavity of Fig. 4-3.

We consider first the last term on the right. The Amperian surface current has a magnitude

$$\mathbf{J}_{MA} = |\mathbf{M} \times \mathbf{n}| = M \sin \theta \tag{4–28}$$

where the geometrical relationships are shown in Fig. 4–4. Choosing as an element of area the ring of radius $R \sin \theta$ and width $R\,d\theta$, the current in this element is given by

$$dI = J_{MA} R\,d\theta = M \sin \theta\,(R\,d\theta) \tag{4–29}$$

By (3–37), the induction on the axis of this circular loop is

$$B = \mu_v \frac{I}{2} \frac{(R \sin \theta)^2}{R^3}$$

so that for the entire sphere

$$B = \int_0^\pi \frac{\mu_v}{2} \frac{\sin^2 \theta}{R} MR \sin \theta\,d\theta = \frac{2}{3}\mu_v M$$

The direction of **B** comes from the fact that the direction of the current in the ring-element is given by **M × n**, which establishes an induction **B** opposite to the direction of **M**. This can be seen from Fig. 3–5 and the relation (3–34), which we write in the form

$$\mathbf{B} = \frac{\mu_v}{4\pi} \int \frac{(I\,d\mathbf{l}) \times \mathbf{r}_0}{r^2}$$

Problem 4-4

Redraw Fig. 3-6 with the resultant induction **B** lying to the left of the loop and show that the geometrical arrangement agrees with Fig. 4-4.

Hence,

$$\mathbf{B} = \frac{-2}{3}\mu_v \mathbf{M} \tag{4–30}$$

We now wish to evaluate $\mathbf{B}_v''$ in (4–27). We consider a small current loop of moment **m** located for convenience at the center of the sphere, and set up the following integral

$$\int \mathbf{B}\, dV = \int \mathbf{curl\ A}\, dV \tag{4–31}$$

where we will not carry the primes in the following short discussion. Now using

$$\mathbf{A} = \frac{\mu_v}{4\pi r^2}\mathbf{m} \times \mathbf{r}_0 \tag{4–9}$$

and the generalized Gauss theorem

$$\int \mathbf{curl\ F}\, dV = \oint d\mathbf{A} \times \mathbf{F} = \oint dA\mathbf{n} \times \mathbf{F} \tag{A–13}$$

we can convert (4–31) into the surface integral given by

$$\int \mathbf{B}\, dV = \frac{\mu_v}{4\pi}\oint \frac{\mathbf{n} \times (\mathbf{m} \times \mathbf{r}_0)}{R^2}\, dA \tag{4–32}$$

Applying

$$\mathbf{A} \times (\mathbf{B} \times \mathbf{C}) = \mathbf{B}(\mathbf{A}\cdot\mathbf{C}) - \mathbf{C}(\mathbf{A}\cdot\mathbf{B}) \tag{A–1}$$

Eq. (4–32) becomes

$$\int \mathbf{B}\, dV = \frac{\mu_v}{4\pi}\oint \left[\frac{\mathbf{m}(\mathbf{n}\cdot\mathbf{r}_0) - \mathbf{r}_0(\mathbf{n}\cdot\mathbf{m})}{R^2}\, dA\right] \tag{4–33}$$

The geometrical arrangement for evaluating these integrals is shown in Fig. 4–5, and we see that

$$\oint \frac{\mathbf{m}(\mathbf{n}\cdot\mathbf{r}_0)\, dA}{R^2} = \mathbf{m}\oint \frac{dA}{R^2} = 4\pi\mathbf{m}$$

For the second integral, we have

$$\mathbf{n}\cdot\mathbf{m} = \mathbf{m}\cos\theta$$

and

$$\mathbf{r}_0 = (\mathbf{i}\sin\theta\cos\varphi + \mathbf{j}\sin\theta\sin\varphi + \mathbf{k}\cos\theta) \tag{4–34}$$

where θ and φ are spherical coordinates.

Problem 4-5
Verify (4-34).

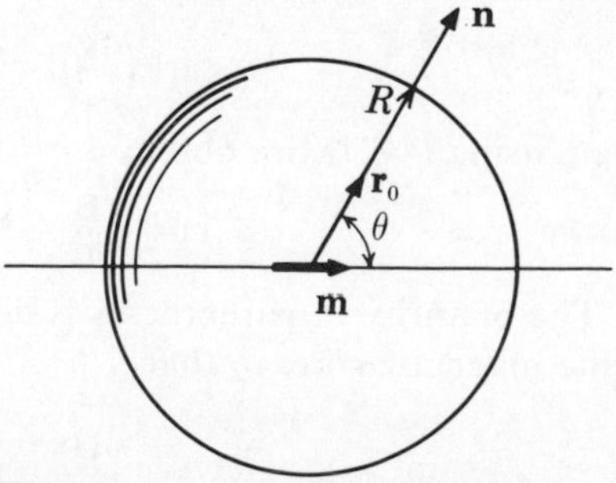

Fig. 4-5 Evaluation of the integrals involving Amperian currents.

Then

$$\int_0^{2\pi}\int_0^{\pi} \frac{(\mathbf{i}\sin\theta\cos\varphi + \mathbf{j}\sin\theta\sin\varphi + \mathbf{k}\cos\theta)}{R^2}(\mathbf{m}\cos\theta)R^2\sin\theta\, d\theta\, d\varphi$$

$$= \frac{4\pi}{3}\mathbf{m} \tag{4–35}$$

Substituting this result into (4–33) gives

$$\int \mathbf{B}\, dV = \frac{\mu_v}{4\pi}\left(4\pi\mathbf{m} - \frac{4\pi}{3}\mathbf{m}\right) = \frac{2}{3}\mu_v\mathbf{m} \tag{4–36}$$

so that this term exactly cancels the last term of (4–27), in accordance with (4–30). Hence, (4–27) reduces to

$$\mathbf{B}_M = \frac{\mu_v}{4\pi}\int \frac{\mathbf{J}_M \times \mathbf{r}_0'}{r'^2}\, dV' + \frac{\mu_v}{4\pi}\oint \frac{\mathbf{J}_M \times \mathbf{r}_0'}{r'^2}\, dA$$

which is identical to (4–26) and shows that the use of Amperian currents gives the correct value of **B** outside or inside the material.

4.3 Magnetic Susceptibility and Permeability

Consider the toroidal winding of Fig. 3–15 into which we can insert cores of various kinds of magnetic materials (such an arrangement is usually known as a *Rowland ring*). We have already shown that the induction due to the current in an air-core toroid is

$$\mathbf{B}_0 = \frac{\mu_v nI}{2\pi R} \tag{3–85}$$

If we now place a core inside the toroid and find a new value **B** of the induction which differs from $\mathbf{B}_0$, we can ascribe this to the magnetization in the material, which in turn can be expressed in terms of an Amperian current. Let us recall the Maxwell equation (3–83), which has the form

$$\textbf{curl}\left(\frac{\mathbf{B}}{\mu_v}\right) = \mathbf{J} + \frac{\partial \mathbf{D}}{\partial t} \tag{4–37}$$

Let us now include an additional term which incorporates the Amperian current $\mathbf{J}_M$ (where this quantity represents both surface and volume currents combined). Hence

$$\text{curl}\left(\frac{\mathbf{B}}{\mu_v}\right) = \mathbf{J} + \frac{\partial \mathbf{D}}{\partial t} + \mathbf{J}_M \tag{4–38}$$

Then, using (4–21), we obtain

$$\text{curl}\left(\frac{\mathbf{B}}{\mu_v} - \mathbf{M}\right) = \mathbf{J} + \frac{\partial \mathbf{D}}{\partial t} \tag{4–39}$$

The quantity in parentheses is defined as the *magnetic field intensity* **H** in the magnetic core, so that

$$\mathbf{H} = \frac{\mathbf{B}}{\mu_v} - \mathbf{M}$$

or

$$\mathbf{B} = \mu_v(\mathbf{H} + \mathbf{M}) \tag{4–40}$$

is the magnetic equivalent of the definition (2–29), but we note that they are not quite the same in form. The quantity **H** has the same units as **M**, namely, dipole moment per unit volume, and it also has ampere/meter as units.

Problem 4-6

Verify the last statement above.

In analogy with the discussion of Sec. 2.3, we can define a *magnetic susceptibility* κ by

$$\mathbf{M} = \kappa\mathbf{H} \tag{4–41}$$

so that

$$\begin{aligned}\mathbf{B} &= \mu_v(1 + \kappa)\mathbf{H} \\ &= \mu_v\mu_r\,\mathbf{H}\end{aligned} \tag{4–42}$$

where $\mu_r = (1 + \kappa)$ is the *magnetic coefficient* of the medium. It is possible for κ to be less than 1.0, in which case the material is said to be *diamagnetic*. When κ is greater than 1.0, the medium is called *paramagnetic*.

Problem 4-7

A spherical shell with radii a and $b (a < b)$ is magnetized in such a way that M inside the shell is spherically symmetrical and has the form

$$\mathbf{M} = \frac{M_0\mathbf{i}_r}{r}$$

where M_0 is a constant.

(a) Calculate the equivalent Amperian currents.

(b) Find **B**, **H**, and **M** for all values of r.

4.4 The Magnetic Circuit

Once again, let us consider a toroid (Fig. 3-15) composed of a magnetic core with a winding of n turns. We will assume that the magnetic field established by the current I is confined to the interior of the core, and that the field is approximately uniform across the core. Weber's law (3–88) can then be written in the form

$$\oint H\,dl = nI \tag{4–43}$$

since **B** and **H** are tangential to circles concentric with the center of the toroid. If we now introduce the magnetic flux into this equation through the use of the relations

$$\Phi = \int \mathbf{B}\cdot d\mathbf{A} \tag{3–53}$$

or

$$\Phi = BA \tag{4–44}$$

for a uniform field in a toroid of cross section A, and

$$\mathbf{B} = \mu_r \mu_v H \tag{4–42}$$

we obtain

$$\frac{\Phi}{\mu_r \mu_v A} \int dl = \frac{\Phi_l}{\mu_r \mu_v A} = nI \tag{4–45}$$

where $l = 2\pi R$ is the average path length. Writing (4–45) in the form

$$\Phi = \frac{nI}{\left(\dfrac{l}{\mu_r \mu_v A}\right)} \tag{4–46}$$

we obtain a magnetic analogue of Ohm's law

$$I = \frac{V}{R} \tag{3–3}$$

That is, the quantity $l/\mu_r \mu_v A$, called the *reluctance* $\mathscr{R}$, has the same form as (3–5) so that $\mu_r \mu_v$ corresponds to σ, and we have the definition

$$\mathscr{R} = \frac{l}{\mu_r \mu_v A} \tag{4–47}$$

The term nI is called the *magnetomotance* $\mathscr{F}$ and by Weber's law, it can be expressed as

$$\mathscr{F} = \oint \mathbf{H} \cdot d\mathbf{l} = nI$$

which is similar to (1–34). In addition, we see that flux and current are corresponding quantities, so that the "Ohm's law" for magnetic circuits is

$$\Phi = \frac{\mathscr{F}}{\mathscr{R}} \tag{4–48}$$

Example 4-1 The Electromagnet

The electromagnet of Fig. 4–6, has an effective closed magnetic path-length l, a gap-width of g, pole faces of area A, and is wound with n turns. The reluctance of the core is then

$$\mathscr{R}_C = \frac{l - g}{\mu_r \mu_v A}$$

and of the gap is

$$\mathscr{R}_G = \frac{g}{\mu_v A}$$

so that the total reluctance is

$$\mathscr{R} = \frac{l - g}{\mu_r \mu_v A} + \frac{g}{\mu_v A}$$

We are assuming here that the gap-width is small compared with the core dimensions, so that the lines of force do not spread out. In addition, if we assume that the permeability of iron is high, so that $\mu_r \gg 1$, then

$$\mathscr{R} = \frac{\dfrac{l}{\mu_r} + g}{\mu_v A} = \frac{g}{\mu_v A} \qquad (4\text{–}49)$$

The flux is then

$$\Phi = \frac{nI}{\mathscr{R}} = \frac{nI\mu_v A}{g} \qquad (4\text{–}50)$$

and the inductance of the magnet is

$$L = \frac{d\Phi}{dI} = \frac{n\mu_v A}{g} \qquad (4\text{–}51)$$

We note that (4–49) tells us that the reluctance is primarily due to the gap, in analogy with the case of a large and a small resistance in series.

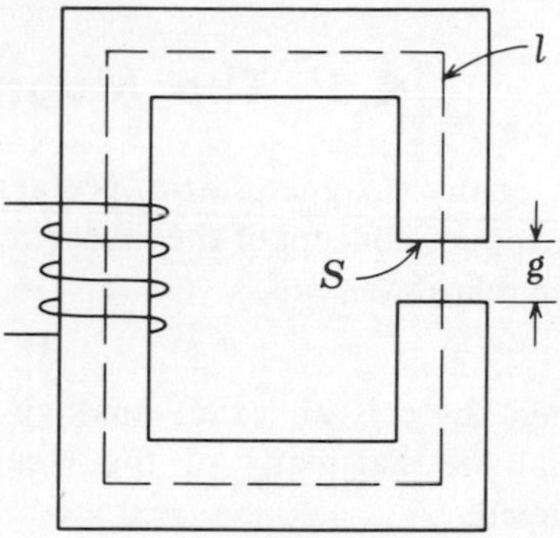

Fig. 4-6 A magnetic circuit.

Example 4-2 The Iron-Core Transformer

The transformer shown in Fig. 4–7a can be converted into the equivalent magnetic circuit of Fig. 4–7b, where

$$\mathscr{R}_1 = \frac{l_1}{\mu_r \mu_v A}$$

$$\mathscr{R}_2 = \frac{l_2}{\mu_r \mu_v A}$$

$$\mathscr{R}_g = \frac{g}{\mu_v A}$$

Writing mesh equations in analogy with electrical circuits, we obtain

$$n_1 I = \mathscr{F} = \Phi_1(\mathscr{R}_1 + 2\mathscr{R}_2 + \mathscr{R}_g) - \Phi_2(2\mathscr{R}_2 + \mathscr{R}_g)$$
$$0 = \Phi_1(2\mathscr{R}_2 + \mathscr{R}_g) - \Phi_2(\mathscr{R}_1 + 2\mathscr{R}_2 + \mathscr{R}_g)$$

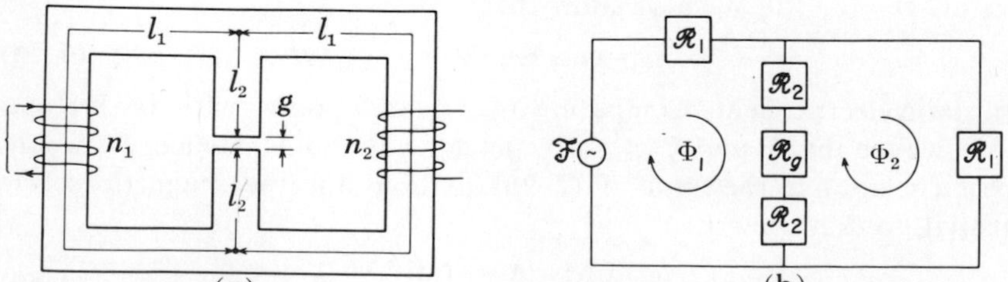

(a) (b)

Fig. 4-7 (a) An iron-core transformer. (b) The equivalent magnetic circuit of the transformer (from Robert Plonsey and Robert E. Collin, Principles and Applications of Electromagnetic Fields, McGraw-Hill Book Co., Inc., 1961, with permission.)

from which

$$\Phi_2 = \frac{n_1 I(2\mathscr{R}_2 + \mathscr{R}_g)}{\mathscr{R}_1(\mathscr{R}_1 + 4\mathscr{R}_2 + 2\mathscr{R}_g)} \tag{4-52}$$

4.5 The Magnetic Scalar Potential

Many magnetostatic problems can be conveniently handled if we introduce concept of the *magnetic scalar potential* V_M. If we define it through the relation

$$\mathbf{H} = -\mathbf{grad}\, V_M \tag{4-53}$$

then there is an exact analogy with the electrostatic potential V, and we shall see that many of the results of electrostatics can be carried over directly.

Let us consider a situation where the magnetic effects are due only to a permanent magnetization $\mathbf{M}$, such as the field of a bar magnet. Then by the Maxwell equation (3–83), we have

$$\mathbf{curl\, B} = \mathbf{curl\, H} = 0 \tag{4-54}$$

Turning to (4–40), we have

$$\text{div}\, \mathbf{H} = -\text{div}\, \mathbf{M} \tag{4-55}$$

since div $\mathbf{B} = 0$.

Now it was shown in Chap. 2 that the electric polarization $\mathbf{P}$ can be expressed as

$$\mathbf{P} = \mathbf{D} - \epsilon_v \mathbf{E} \tag{2-29}$$

so that

$$\text{div}\, \mathbf{P} = \text{div}\, \mathbf{D} - \epsilon_v\, \text{div}\, \mathbf{E} \tag{4-56}$$

If the electric field $\mathbf{E}$ is due solely to polarization charges and there is no volume charge ρ present, then

$$-\text{div}\, \mathbf{P} = \epsilon_v\, \text{div}\, \mathbf{E} \tag{4-57}$$

since div $\mathbf{D} = \rho = 0$. We also know that

$$\mathbf{curl\, E} = 0 \tag{4-58}$$

for a static electric field. Comparing (4–57) and (4–58) with (4–54) and (4–55), we see that $\mathbf{E}$ and $\mathbf{P}/\epsilon_v$ correspond to $\mathbf{H}$ and $\mathbf{M}$. Hence, we would expect a relation of the form of (2–26) to hold for the magnetic scalar potential, so that we write

$$V_M = \frac{\mu_v}{4\pi}\left[\oint \frac{\mathbf{M}\cdot d\mathbf{A}}{\bar{r}} - \int \frac{\text{div}\, \mathbf{M}}{\bar{r}}\, dV\right] \tag{4-59}$$

and then, in analogy with (2–27), we define *equivalent magnetic charges* by the relations

$$q_{MA} = M_n, \qquad q_{MV} = -\text{div}\, \mathbf{M} \tag{4-60}$$

The equivalent magnetic charge is a fictitious quantity, but one which is equivalent to—and as useful as—the concept of Amperian currents. In the development of magnetic theory, it was believed that magnetic effects were concentrated at points called *poles*, like the north and south poles of a bar magnet, and the quantitative specification of the properties of a pole was given in terms of the *pole strength,* which is what we call here the equivalent magnetic charge q_M. We now realize that magnetic forces are due either to the motion of electric charges in conductors or to the properties of the elementary electron charges in magnetic materials. However, the concept of magnetic point-poles is a convenient approximation, provided that we remember that it is valid only when we are working at distances which are large compared to the separation of the fictitious poles.

Example 4-3 The Cylindrical Bar Magnet

A cylindrical bar magnet with a uniform polarization M parallel to the axis is shown in Fig. 4–8. Since $\mathbf{M}$ is a constant, then $\operatorname{div} \mathbf{M} = 0$; and by (4–60), we have only an equivalent surface charge q_{MS}. This quantity has no contribution from the sides since there is no normal component of $\mathbf{M}$. For the ends, q_{MS} is M at $L/2$ and $-M$ at $-L/2$. The corresponding magnetic charges are then

$$q_M = \pm M(\pi R^2) \qquad \textbf{(4–61)}$$

At a large distance from the magnet ($r' \gg R$), we can regard these charges as being concentrated at points at the center of each face. Then we may use the electrostatic analogy to obtain V_M as

$$V_M = \frac{q_M}{4\pi}\left(\frac{1}{\bar{r}_1} - \frac{1}{\bar{r}_2}\right)$$
$$= \frac{\pi R^2 M}{4\pi}\left(\frac{1}{\bar{r}_1} - \frac{1}{\bar{r}_2}\right) \qquad \textbf{(4–62)}$$

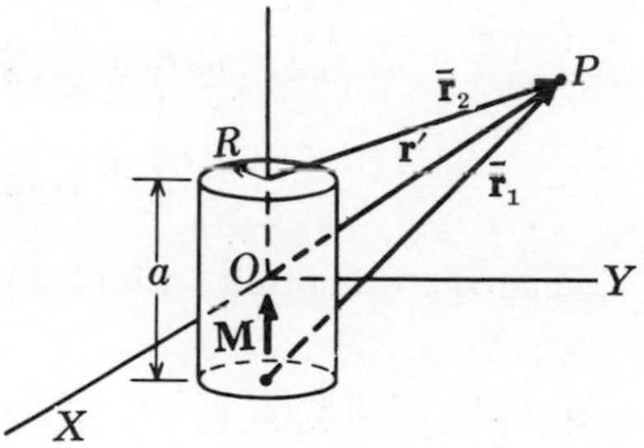

Fig. 4-8 The field of a cylindrical bar magnet.

Problem 4-8
Verify that (4-62) is dimensionally consistent.

The field $\mathbf{H}$ is then

$$\mathbf{H} = -\mathbf{grad}'\, V_M = -\frac{R^2 M}{4}\,\mathbf{grad}'\left(\frac{1}{\bar{r}_1} - \frac{1}{\bar{r}_2}\right) \qquad \textbf{(4–63)}$$

where we must prime the gradient operator to show explicitly that we are differentiating $\bar{r}_1$ and $\bar{r}_2$ with respect to the field-point coordinates. It is interesting to see that we get the same answer by using the idea of Amperian currents. In order to do this, we first consider a real solenoid of the same dimensions as the magnet (Fig. 4–9). The field **B** is given by Eq. (4–13) which, when modified to have the source point at the location $\mathbf{r} = z\mathbf{k}$, becomes

$$\mathbf{B} = \frac{\mu_v}{4\pi} \,\mathbf{grad}' \left[\mathbf{m} \cdot \mathbf{grad}' \left(\frac{1}{\bar{r}}\right)\right] \tag{4-64}$$

Now consider this solenoid to be composed of a stack of current-loops of height a. If there are n_l turns per unit length, the dipole moment of a section of thickness dz, by (4–8), is

$$d\mathbf{m} = n_l\, dz\, I\pi R^2 \mathbf{k}$$

and the field becomes

$$\mathbf{B} = \frac{\mu_v}{4\pi} \,\mathbf{grad}' \int_{-a/2}^{a/2} n_l\, dz\, I\, \pi R^2 \mathbf{k} \cdot \mathbf{grad}' \left(\frac{1}{\bar{r}}\right) \tag{4-65}$$

But

$$\mathbf{grad}' \left(\frac{1}{\bar{r}}\right) = -\frac{\bar{\mathbf{r}}}{\bar{r}^3} \tag{2-20}$$

so that (4–65) becomes

$$\begin{aligned} \mathbf{B} &= -\frac{n_l I R^2 \mu_v}{4} \,\mathbf{grad}' \int_{-a/2}^{a/2} \frac{(z' - z)\, dz}{[x^2 + y^2 + (z' - z)^2]^{3/2}} \\ &= -\frac{n_l I R^2 \mu_v}{4} \,\mathbf{grad}' \left[x^2 + y^2 + (z' - z)^2\right]^{-1/2} \Big|_{-a/2}^{a/2} \\ &= -\frac{n_l I R^2 \mu_v}{4} \,\mathbf{grad}' \left(\frac{1}{\bar{r}}\right) \Big|_{-a/2}^{a/2} \\ &= -\frac{n_l I R^2 \mu_v}{4} \,\mathbf{grad}' \left(\frac{1}{\bar{r}_1} - \frac{1}{\bar{r}_2}\right) \end{aligned} \tag{4-66}$$

Comparing this result with (4–63) shows that

$$M = n_l I \tag{4-67}$$

and the dipole moment of the solenoid then has a magnitude given by

$$m = MV = n_l I(\pi R^2 a) = nI\pi R^2$$

which is what we would expect from (4–8). For the cylindrical magnet, we have no Amperian volume current by (4–21), since **M** is a constant. The surface Amperian current is given by (4–22) and flows circumferentially around the magnet (like the real current in the solenoid). Hence the solenoid and the two fictitious forms of the bar magnet are all equivalent.

We can use these results to get an insight into the physical meaning of Amperian currents. From the definition

$$\mathbf{J}_M = \mathbf{curl}\, \mathbf{M} \tag{4-21}$$

we see that the volume current represents the circulation of the magnetization. That is, the volume currents can be regarded as a series of current-loops (Fig. 4–10) whose properties depend on the variation of **M** over the cross-sectional plane. If **M** is uniform, then $\mathbf{J}_M$ vanishes in the interior as

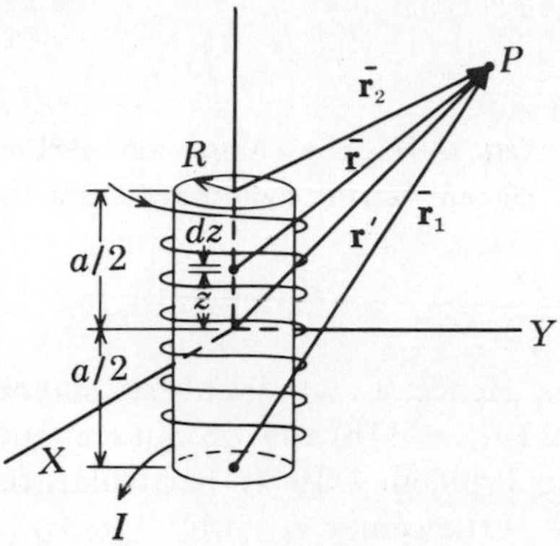

Fig. 4-9 A solenoid equivalent to the magnet of Fig. 4-8.

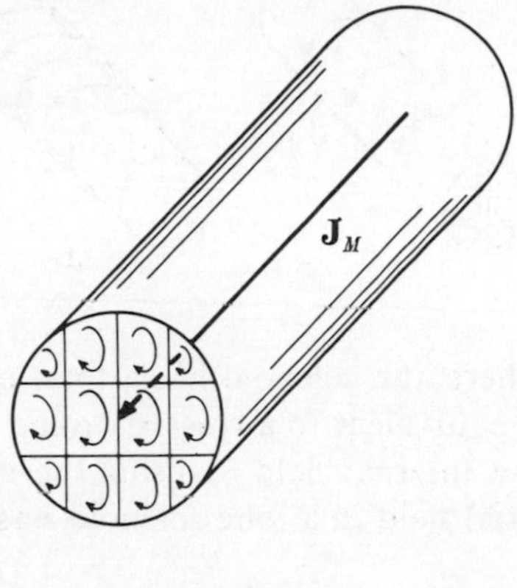

Fig. 4-10 The Amperian volume current for the cylindrical magnet.

we have seen, and we can think of this as being due to the individual current-loops exactly cancelling one another along the interior boundaries. This leaves only a surface current due to the outermost sections of the loops.

Problem 4-9

Consider a magnetized region with an equivalent magnetic volume charge q_{MV} and an equivalent magnetic surface charge q_{MS}. Show that the external field is given by

$$\mathbf{B} = \frac{\mu_v}{4\pi}\left[\int \frac{q_{MV}\,dV}{\bar{r}^2} + \frac{q_{MA}\,dA}{\bar{r}^2}\right]\bar{\mathbf{r}}_0 \tag{4-68}$$

Let us now consider the behavior of the fields inside and outside the cylindrical magnet. If the magnetization **M** is uniform and parallel to the axis, there is no equivalent volume current, since

$$\mathbf{J}_M = \mathbf{curl}\,\mathbf{M} = 0$$

The equivalent surface current, given by

$$\mathbf{J}_{MA} = \mathbf{M} \times \mathbf{n} \tag{4-22}$$

is then tangential to the curved surface, and vanishes over the circular ends (Fig. 4-11a). From our definition of surface current density

$$\mathbf{J}_A = \lim_{\substack{W\to 0\\ J\to\infty}} \mathbf{J}_W \tag{3-140}$$

we see that the surface current on the cylinder wall is related to an equivalent ordinary current by

$$J_A = \frac{nI}{l} \tag{4-69}$$

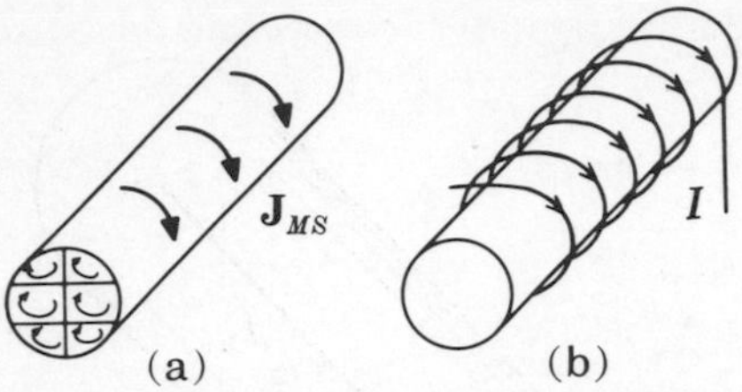

Fig. 4-11 The Amperian surface current for the cylindrical magnet.

where the solenoid has a total of n turns. Hence, a cylindrical bar magnet is equivalent to a closely wound solenoid (Fig. 4–11b) and we can compute the internal field by using the method of Problem 4–10. In particular, the axial field in a long solenoid has a value at the center given by

$$B_x = \mu_v I n_l \tag{3-39}$$

and at the ends it is one-half this value, or

$$B_x = \mu_v I n_l / 2 \tag{3-40}$$

Figure 4–12a shows the field **B** surrounding a solenoid in a vacuum, and we realize that the field **H** has the same appearance. In Fig. 4–12b, we show for comparison the field **H**, which has the same shape in the exterior region for both the solenoid and the permanent magnet and which is also identical to Fig. 4–12a for the external region. To calculate **H** inside the

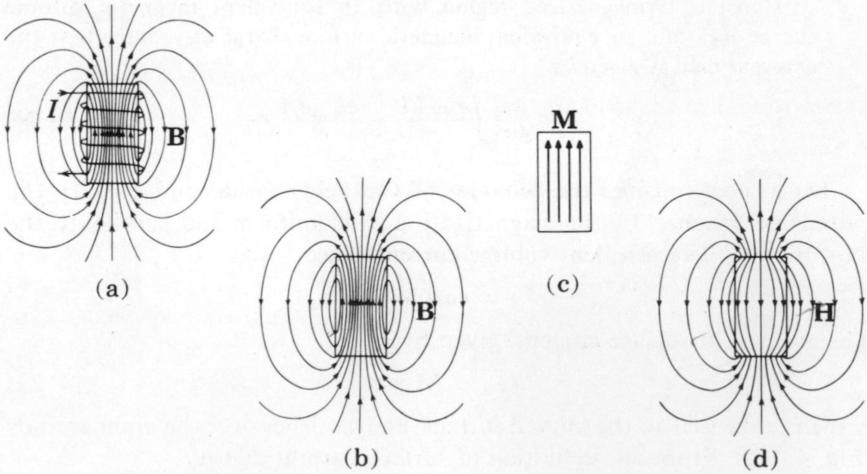

Fig. 4-12 (a) A plot of **B** for an air-core solenoid. (b) An equivalent magnet. (c) The magnetization. (d) A plot of H (after Pugh and Pugh, Principles of Electricity and Magnetism, Addision-Wesley Pub. Co., 1960, with permission.)

magnet, we use the definition (4–40) and the boundary conditions of Sec. 3.9. We also use our previous result

$$M = n_l I \tag{4–67}$$

to convert (3–40) into

$$\mathbf{B}_x = \mu_v \mathbf{M}/2 \tag{4–70}$$

This equation refers to the field just inside the solenoid at its ends. To find the corresponding value of **H** now, we see from (4–40) that

$$\mathbf{H} = (\mathbf{B}/\mu_v) - \mathbf{M}$$

so that

$$\mathbf{H} = -(\mathbf{M}/2) \tag{4–71}$$

This result shows that **B** and **H** are *oppositely* directed along the axis in the interior of the solenoid, as illustrated in Figs. 4–12b and 4–12d. By combining the field pattern of the remainder of Fig. 4–12b with the uniform **M** of Fig. 4–12c, we obtain the complete picture for **H** shown in Fig. 4–12d.

The sketch of **B** in Fig. 4–12b shows an interesting behavior that should be pointed out. Since the normal component must be continuous, the value of $\mathbf{B}_x$ just outside the magnet is the same as just inside. The following problem extends this result:

Problem 4-10

Show that **B** itself is continuous across the end-faces by applying the boundary condition to B_n and H_t to the field at any point on the face.

Similar reasoning can be applied to the curved surface, and Fig. 4–12 is drawn to take account of this property **B**.

4.6 Magnetic Energy

We would now like to establish the relations for magnetic fields which are equivalent to those given for electric fields at the end of Chap. 1. Referring back to the relation for the work done in moving an element of conductor through a magnetic field, it was shown that dW is given by

$$dW = I(\mathbf{B} \cdot d\mathbf{A}) \tag{3–54}$$

or

$$dW = I\, d\Phi \tag{4–72}$$

If we now extend this ~~extend this~~ expression to a group of n circuits, then the electrical work done against the induced fields is

$$dW = \sum_{i=1}^{n} I_i\, d\Phi_i$$

and

$$W = \sum \int I_i\, d\Phi_i \tag{4–73}$$

Now let us assume that all the circuits reach their final value of currents and fluxes at the same rate. This is a permissible assumption, since the total energy involved should be independent of the way in which the current builds up. Using the fraction α which we introduced in Sec. 1.10, we can then write the current at any intermediate step as

$$I_i' = aI_i$$

and the change in flux corresponding to a change in α from α to $\alpha + d\alpha$ as

$$d\Phi_i' = \Phi_i \, da$$

Equation (4–23) then becomes

$$W = \Sigma \int I_i' \, d\Phi_i' = \Sigma \, I_i \Phi_i \int_0^1 \alpha \, d\alpha = \frac{1}{2} \Sigma \, I_i \Phi_i \tag{4–74}$$

and this result is analogous to Eq. (3–66). The quantity $d\Phi_i$ can be written in another way through the use of the definitions of inductance given in Sec. 3.6. Since we have n circuits, each carrying a current I_j, the change dI_j in each of these currents will cause a change in the flux $d\Phi_{1j}$ common to the two circuits and a total change in flux in the circuit 1 given by

$$d\Phi_1 = \frac{d\Phi_{1j}}{dI_1} dI_1 + \frac{d\Phi_{2j}}{dI_2} dI_2 + \cdots$$

or, in general

$$d\Phi_i = \sum_{j=1}^{n} \frac{d\Phi_{ij}}{dI_j} dI_j \tag{4–75}$$

Now our definitions for inductance were

$$L = \frac{d\Phi}{dI} \tag{3–63}$$

and

$$L_{12} = \frac{d\Phi_1}{dI_2} \tag{3–70}$$

so that we may write (4–75) as

$$d\Phi_i = \sum_j L_{ij} \, dI_j \tag{4–76}$$

where it is understood that terms of the form L_{ii}—which we write simply as L_i—represent self-inductance, and terms like L_{ij} are coefficients of mutual inductance. If we impose the requirement on the n circuits that they be fixed in space, and if we assume that the circuits are coupled in such a way that the inductances do not depend on the currents (as would be the case, for example, for iron-core transformers), then the L_{ij} are constants and (4–76) can be integrated to give

$$\Phi_i = \sum_j L_{ij} I_j \tag{4–77}$$

Combining this with (4–74) gives

$$W = \frac{1}{2} \sum_{i,\,j=1}^{n} L_{ij} I_i I_j \tag{4–78}$$

Example 4-4 Two Coupled Circuits

For two coupled circuits, (4–78) reduces to

$$W = \frac{1}{2} L_1 I_1^2 + L_{12} I_1 I_2 + \frac{1}{2} L_2 I_2^2 \tag{4–79}$$

Letting

$$r = \frac{I_1}{I_2}$$

we obtain

$$W = \frac{1}{2} I_2^2 (L_1 r^2 + 2L_{12} r + L_2) \tag{4–80}$$

Differentiating with respect to r, the condition for a maximum or minimum in W is

$$\frac{dW}{dr} = I_2^2 (L_1 r + L_{12}) = 0$$

or

$$r = -\frac{L_{12}}{L_1} \tag{4–81}$$

Further,

$$\frac{d^2 W}{dr^2} = I_2^2 L_1$$

so that $d^2 W/dr^2$ is positive, showing that (4–81) is the condition for a minimum. Since W must be positive or zero, then (4–80) gives

$$L_1 r^2 + 2L_{12} r + L_2 \geqq 0$$

and using (4–81), this becomes

$$L_{12}^2 - 2\frac{L_{12}^2}{L_1} + L^2 \geqq 0$$

or

$$L_1 L_2 \geqq + L_{12}^2 \tag{4–82}$$

This result agrees with the discussion of Ex. 4–11, namely, that the coupling coefficient k has a maximum value of 1.0.

Let us now suppose that each of the n circuits with which we are dealing, has the form of a single, closed loop. The flux Φ_i for each loop can then be expressed as

$$\Phi_i = \int \mathbf{B} \cdot d\mathbf{A}_i = \int \mathbf{A} \cdot d\mathbf{l}_i \tag{4–83}$$

where we have used (3–52). Putting this in (4–74) gives

$$W = \frac{1}{2} \Sigma \int I_i \mathbf{A} \cdot d\mathbf{l}_i \tag{4–84}$$

If each of these loops is actually an arbitrary closed path in some conducting region, then we can still use (4–84) provided that we make the substitution $I_i d\mathbf{l}_i = \mathbf{J}\, dV$ and replace the summation by an integration, obtaining

$$W = \frac{1}{2} \int \mathbf{J} \cdot \mathbf{A}\, dV$$

Using the Maxwell equation (3–83) with $\mathbf{D}$ constant gives

$$\mathbf{J} = \mathbf{curl\, H}$$

so that

$$W = \frac{1}{2} \int \mathbf{curl\, H} \cdot \mathbf{A}\, dV$$

and the vector identity (A–6) converts this into

$$W = \frac{1}{2} \int \mathbf{H} \cdot \mathbf{curl\, A}\, dV - \frac{1}{2} \int \text{div}\, (\mathbf{A} \times \mathbf{H})\, dV$$

The second integral on the right can be converted into a surface integral by the divergence theorem, obtaining

$$\int \text{div}\, (\mathbf{A} \times \mathbf{H})\, dV = \oint \mathbf{A} \times \mathbf{H} \cdot d\mathbf{S}$$

Now a small current-loop at a distance large compared to its diameter is equivalent to a dipole, and we know that the field $\mathbf{H}$ of a dipole falls off as $1/r^2$. Also, $\mathbf{A}$ for a dipole falls off as $1/r$, since $\mathbf{B} = \mathbf{curl\, A}$. Finally, $d\mathbf{A}$ depends directly on r^2, so that the surface integral we have obtained vanishes for large r. Then we are left with

$$W = \frac{1}{2} \int \mathbf{H} \cdot \mathbf{curl\, A}\, dV = \frac{1}{2} \int \mathbf{H} \cdot \mathbf{B}\, dV \tag{4–85}$$

and in the same fashion as Sec. 1.10, we obtain for the magnetic energy-density W_V the expression

$$W_V = \frac{\mu_v}{2} H^2 \tag{4–86}$$

and the total energy-density associated with an electromagnetic wave is

$$W_V = \frac{\epsilon_v E^2 + \mu_v H^2}{2} \tag{4–87}$$

Appendix A

Vector Identities

$$\mathbf{A} \times (\mathbf{B} \times \mathbf{C}) = (\mathbf{A} \cdot \mathbf{C})\mathbf{B} - (\mathbf{A} \cdot \mathbf{B})\mathbf{C} \tag{A-1}$$

$$\mathbf{grad}(AF) = A\,\mathbf{grad}\,F + F\,\mathbf{grad}\,A \tag{A-2}$$

$$\mathrm{div}(A\mathbf{B}) = A\,\mathrm{div}\,\mathbf{B} + \mathbf{B} \cdot \mathbf{grad}\,A \tag{A-3}$$

$$\mathbf{curl}(A\mathbf{B}) = \mathbf{grad}\,A \times \mathbf{B} + A\,\mathbf{curl}\,\mathbf{B} \tag{A-4}$$

$$\mathbf{grad}(\mathbf{A} \cdot \mathbf{B}) = (\mathbf{A} \cdot \mathbf{grad})\mathbf{B} + (\mathbf{B} \cdot \mathbf{grad})\mathbf{A} + \mathbf{A} \times (\mathbf{curl}\,\mathbf{B}) + \mathbf{B} \times (\mathbf{curl}\,\mathbf{A}) \tag{A-5}$$

$$\mathrm{div}(\mathbf{A} \times \mathbf{B}) = \mathbf{B} \cdot (\mathbf{curl}\,\mathbf{A}) - \mathbf{A} \cdot (\mathbf{curl}\,\mathbf{B}) \tag{A-6}$$

$$\mathbf{curl}(\mathbf{A} \times \mathbf{B}) = \mathbf{A}\,\mathrm{div}\,\mathbf{B} - \mathbf{B}\,\mathrm{div}\,\mathbf{A} + (\mathbf{B} \cdot \mathbf{grad})\mathbf{A} - (\mathbf{A} \cdot \mathbf{grad})\mathbf{B} \tag{A-7}$$

$$\mathrm{div}\,\mathbf{curl}\,\mathbf{F} = 0 \tag{A-8}$$

$$\mathbf{curl}\,\mathbf{grad}\,A = 0 \tag{A-9}$$

$$\mathbf{curl}\,\mathbf{curl}\,\mathbf{A} = \mathbf{grad}\,\mathrm{div}\,\mathbf{A} - \nabla^2\mathbf{A} \tag{A-10}$$

Gauss' Theroems

$$\int \mathrm{div}\,\mathbf{F}\,dV = \oint \mathbf{F} \cdot d\mathbf{A} \quad \text{(Divergence Theorem)} \tag{A-11}$$

$$\int \mathbf{grad}\,F\,dV = \oint F\,d\mathbf{A} \tag{A-12}$$

$$\int \mathbf{curl}\,\mathbf{F}\,dV = \oint d\mathbf{A} \times \mathbf{F} \tag{A-13}$$

Stokes' Theorems

$$\int \mathbf{curl}\,\mathbf{F} \cdot d\mathbf{A} = \oint \mathbf{F} \cdot d\mathbf{l} \tag{A-14}$$

$$\int (d\mathbf{A} \times \mathbf{grad})F = \oint F\,d\mathbf{l} \tag{A-15}$$

$$\int (d\mathbf{A} \times \mathbf{grad}) \times \mathbf{F} = \oint d\mathbf{l} \times \mathbf{F} \tag{A-16}$$

Displacement or Taylor's Theorem

$$f(\mathbf{r}_0 + \mathbf{d}) = e^{d \cdot grad} f(\mathbf{r}_0) \tag{A-17}$$

Spherical Coordinates

$$\left.\begin{aligned}\mathrm{grad}_r\, V &= \frac{\partial V}{\partial r}\\ \mathrm{grad}_\theta\, V &= \frac{1}{r}\frac{\partial V}{\partial \theta}\\ \mathrm{grad}_\varphi\, V &= \frac{1}{r\sin\theta}\frac{\partial V}{\partial \varphi}\end{aligned}\right\} \tag{A–18}$$

$$\mathrm{div}\,\mathbf{E} = \frac{1}{r^2}\frac{\partial}{\partial r}(r^2 E_r) + \frac{1}{r\sin\theta}\frac{\partial}{\partial\theta}(\sin\theta\, E_\theta) + \frac{1}{r\sin\theta}\frac{\partial E_\varphi}{\partial\varphi} \tag{A–19}$$

$$\left.\begin{aligned}\mathrm{curl}_r\,\mathbf{A} &= \frac{1}{r\sin\theta}\left[\frac{\partial}{\partial\theta}(A_\varphi\sin\theta) - \frac{\partial A_\theta}{\partial\varphi}\right]\\ \mathrm{curl}_\theta\,\mathbf{A} &= \frac{1}{r}\left[\frac{1}{\sin\theta}\frac{\partial A_r}{\partial\varphi} - \frac{\partial}{\partial r}(rA_\varphi)\right]\\ \mathrm{curl}_\varphi\,\mathbf{A} &= \frac{1}{r}\left[\frac{\partial}{\partial r}(rA_\theta) - \frac{\partial A_r}{\partial\theta}\right]\end{aligned}\right\} \tag{A–20}$$

$$\mathrm{div}\,\mathbf{grad}\,V = \frac{1}{r^2}\frac{\partial}{\partial r}\left(r^2\frac{\partial V}{\partial r}\right) + \frac{1}{r^2\sin\theta}\frac{\partial}{\partial\theta}\left(\sin\theta\frac{\partial V}{\partial\theta}\right) + \frac{1}{r^2\sin^2\theta}\frac{\partial^2 V}{\partial\varphi^2} \tag{A–21}$$

Cylindrical Coordinates

$$\left.\begin{aligned}\mathrm{grad}_r\, V &= \frac{\partial V}{\partial r}\\ \mathrm{grad}_\theta\, V &= \frac{1}{r}\frac{\partial V}{\partial \theta}\\ \mathrm{grad}_z\, V &= \frac{\partial V}{\partial z}\end{aligned}\right\} \tag{A–22}$$

$$\mathrm{div}\,\mathbf{A} = \frac{\partial A_r}{\partial r} + \frac{1}{r}\frac{\partial A_\theta}{\partial\theta} + \frac{\partial Az}{\partial z} \tag{A–23}$$

$$\left.\begin{aligned}\mathrm{curl}_r\,\mathbf{A} &= \frac{1}{r}\left(\frac{\partial A_z}{\partial\theta} - \frac{\partial}{\partial z}(rA_\theta)\right)\\ \mathrm{curl}_\theta\,\mathbf{A} &= \frac{\partial A_r}{\partial z} - \frac{\partial A_z}{\partial r}\\ \mathrm{curl}_z\,\mathbf{A} &= \frac{1}{r}\left(\frac{\partial}{\partial r}(rA_\theta) - \frac{\partial A_r}{\partial\theta}\right)\end{aligned}\right\} \tag{A–24}$$

$$\mathrm{div}\,\mathbf{grad}\,V = \frac{\partial^2 V}{\partial r^2} + \frac{1}{r}\frac{\partial V}{\partial r} + \frac{1}{r^2}\frac{\partial^2 V}{\partial\theta^2} + \frac{\partial^2 V}{\partial z^2} \tag{A–25}$$

Appendix B

Electromagnetic Quantities

Quantity	Dimensions m	l	t	q	Units	Symbol
Acceleration	0	1	−2	0	meters/second^2	**a**
Angle	0	0	0	0	radians	θ
Area	0	2	0	0	meters^2	A
Capacitance	−1	−2	2	2	farads	C
Charge	0	0	0	1	coulombs	q
Conductivity	−1	−3	1	2	mhos/meter	σ
Current	0	0	−1	1	amperes	I
Current-density	0	−2	−1	1	amperes/meter^2	**J**
Density	1	−3	0	0	kilograms/meter^3	ρ
Dielectric coefficient	0	0	0	0		ϵ_r
Displacement	0	1	0	0	meters	l
Displacement, electric	0	−2	0	1	coulombs/meter^2	**D**
Energy	1	2	−2	0	joules	E
Field intensity, electric	1	1	−2	−1	volts/meter	**E**
Field intensity, magnetic	0	−1	−1	1	amperes/meter	**H**
Flux, electric	0	0	0	1	coulombs	ψ
Flux, magnetic	1	2	−1	−1	webers	Φ
Flux density, electric	0	−2	0	1	coulombs/meter^2	**D**
Flux density, magnetic	1	0	−1	−1	webers/meter^2	**B**
Force	1	1	−2	0	newtons	**F**
Frequency	0	0	−1	0	cycles/second	f
Impedence	1	2	−1	−2	ohms	Z
Inductance	1	2	0	−2	henrys	L
Induction, magnetic	1	0	−1	−1	webers/meter^2	**B**
Length	0	1	0	0	meters	l
Magnetization	0	−1	−1	1	amperes/meter	**M**
Magnetic coefficient	0	0	0	0		μ_r

Quantity	Dimensions				Units	Symbol
	m	l	t	q		
Magnetomotance.........	0	0	−1	1	amperes	$\mathscr{M}$
Mass....................	1	0	0	0	kilograms	m
Moment, electric dipole...	0	1	0	1	coulomb-meters	$\mathbf{P}$
Moment, magnetic dipole.	0	2	−1	1	ampere-meters^2	$\mathbf{m}$
Momentum..............	1	1	−1	0	kilogram-meters/sec	$\mathbf{P}$
Permeability............	1	1	0	−2	henrys/meter	μ
Permittivity.............	−1	−3	2	2	farads/meter	ϵ
Polarization, electric.....	0	−2	0	1	coulombs/meter^2	$\mathbf{P}$
Polarization, magnetic....	0	−1	−1	1	amperes/meter	$\mathbf{M}$
Potential, electric........	1	2	−2	−1	volts	V
Potential, magnetic vector.	1	1	−1	−1	webers/meter	$\mathbf{A}$
Potential, magnetic scalar.	0	0	−1	1	amperes	V_M
Poynting's vector........	1	0	−3	0	watts/meter^2	$\mathbf{P}$
Power....................	1	2	−3	0	watts	P
Reluctance, magnetic.....	−1	−2	0	2	amperes/weber	$\mathscr{R}$
Resistance..............	1	2	−1	−2	ohms	R
Resistivity..............	1	3	1	2	ohm-meters	ρ
Susceptibility, electric....	0	0	0	0		η
Susceptibility, magnetic...	0	0	0	0		κ
Time....................	0	0	1	0	seconds	t
Velocity, angular.........	0	0	−1	0	cycles/second	$\boldsymbol{\omega}$
Velocity, linear..........	0	1	−1	0	meters/second	$\mathbf{v}$
Voltage..................	1	2	−2	−1	volts	$\mathbf{V}$
Volume..................	0	3	0	0	meters^3	V
Work....................	1	2	−2	0	joules	W

Index